THE INTERNATIONAL
WILDLIFE
ENCYCLOPEDIA

VOLUME 20

THE INTERNATIONAL
WILDLIFE
ENCYCLOPEDIA

GENERAL EDITORS

Dr. Maurice Burton

Robert Burton

MARSHALL CAVENDISH CORPORATION / NEW YORK

CONTENTS

SPECIAL CONTENTS

INDEXES

Wryneck

The wryneck is a relative of the woodpeckers but resembles the nightjars in appearance and at a distance can be mistaken for a thrush, especially when it feeds on the ground. It is about 6½ in. long, a little larger than a house sparrow, of slight build and mottled grey-brown plumage. The wryneck is thought to be the most primitive of the woodpecker family as it lacks the stiff tail feathers which woodpeckers use as a prop when climbing and its bill is weak and incapable of chiselling into trees. However, wrynecks have one toe facing sideways to assist climbing and have long hyoid bones supporting the tongue which run back under the skull and over the top of the cranium, features typical of woodpeckers.

The common wryneck ranges across Europe and Asia from southern England to Japan, being widely distributed in Europe except for the extreme north and the extreme southwest and southeast. It is also found in parts of North Africa. The plumage is brown, delicately mottled and streaked with grey and black and the underparts are barred. The chestnut-breasted wryneck of tropical Africa is similar to the Eurasian species except that the throat and breast are rich chestnut and the belly is pale with brown streaks.

▽ *Contortionist: balanced precariously a wryneck twists its head right round to see what is happening behind it. Wrynecks perform this extraordinary trick especially when they are frightened. This species is the African chestnut-breasted wryneck, so called because of its distinctively coloured feather collar.*

Peter Johnson

Dependent on ants

Wyrnecks feed on insects, particularly ants and their pupae, and beetles, butterflies, moths and their larvae. Nestling wrynecks are often fed entirely on the pupae and workers of the common black and yellow ants. During dry weather, when the pupae are carried farther below ground, the nestlings may go short of food. Wrynecks occasionally chase flying insects but usually pick up insects from crevices in bark or in the ground or wipe insects off the surface of leaves with their long tongues.

Brought up on ants

During courtship the pair 'gape' at each other, displaying their pink mouths and writhing and wriggling their necks in the manner that earned them their name. They have occasionally been reported as drumming like woodpeckers.

The usual nest site of wrynecks is a hole in a tree. They are unable to bore their own holes, and have to rely on natural ones. They also use nest-boxes and holes in banks or in walls. The 5–12, usually 7–10, dull white eggs are laid on the unlined floor of the hole. Both parents incubate the eggs until they hatch after 12 days. The chicks are fed by both parents on insects, nearly always ants, brought in the bill.

Vanishing wrynecks

At one time the wryneck was common enough in Britain to have over a score of local names. At present, the wryneck is one of Britain's rarest breeding birds—only about 50 pairs are reported each year, mainly in the southeast. A decline in wryneck population has also occurred in many European countries, but the British wrynecks have suffered worse, perhaps because Britain is at the extreme end of their range.

It is difficult to give a reason for the decline in wrynecks. Like other hole-nesting birds they may be short of nesting sites because of land clearance and increased ploughing may have severely affected ant populations. There is, however, no conclusive evidence for this. Whatever the reason, the wryneck and some European birds are showing a decrease, while others, such as the collared dove (p 485), are increasing. Often the causes of the changes are unknown or improperly known, and this makes it very difficult to assess the effects of man's activities on animals; a decline in numbers of a species is not necessarily evidence of pollution or over-hunting.

Eric Hosking

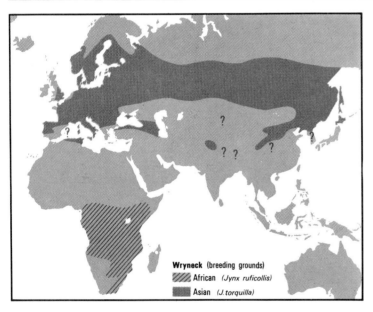

Wryneck (breeding grounds)
- African *(Jynx ruficollis)*
- Asian *(J. torquilla)*

△ *Flying away with a faecal pellet, an Asian wryneck dutifully cleans its nest.*
▽ *A juicy beakful: an Asian wryneck brings ant pupae for its young. Note the wryneck's third eyelid, known as a nictitating membrane. It lies underneath the eyelid on the nasal side, and can be drawn horizontally across the eye. It is usually transparent in diurnal birds like the wryneck, and can be drawn across the eye to moisten or clean it without shutting out the light.*

Cuckoo's mate

The wryneck gets its strange name from its habit of twisting its head round over its back when frightened; an old name for it was snakebird because of the resemblance of this action to a snake waving its neck. A third name for the wryneck was 'cuckoo's mate', because it arrives from its winter quarters in Africa and India at the same time as the cuckoo. Like the cuckoo it is more often heard than seen, its call of 'quee-quee-quee-quee—' sounding like the shrill notes of a kestrel. Wrynecks spend most of their time in the trees but also feed on the ground, as do some true woodpeckers. Although they lack the spiny tail feathers of a true woodpecker, they sometimes use the tail as a prop. They climb very easily on tree trunks and hide by running to the other side of the trunk. When disturbed they fly fairly slowly on an undulating course.

Arthur Christiansen

class	**Aves**
order	**Piciformes**
family	**Picidae**
genus & species	*Jynx ruficollis* African wryneck *J. torquilla* Asian wryneck

X-ray fish

Many small tropical freshwater fishes are semi-transparent, but one particular species has been called the X-ray fish because it is almost totally transparent. The swimbladder and much of the skeleton can be seen but the stomach and intestine are opaque and the hind part of the body is semi-opaque.

X-ray fishes are up to 2 in. long. The body is fairly deep and ends in a forked tailfin. The first dorsal fin is high and so is the long-based anal fin. The second dorsal is very small and the pectoral and pelvic fins are of only moderate size. Although the body is usually described as transparent it sometimes appears silvery in reflected light. At other times it has a faint yellowish or a greenish tinge and there is a black shoulder spot. The first dorsal and the anal fins are lemon yellow with a prominent black blotch or band and they are white at the tips. The tailfin is reddish. The combination of red, black and yellow in the fins recalls the more prominent colours of the goldfinch and another common name used for this species is water goldfinch.

The X-ray fish lives in the rivers of northeastern South America, from the Amazon Basin to the Orinoco River and the Guianas.

Jerky swimmers

These small fishes live mostly in shoals that swim rapidly backwards and forwards. When in smaller groups they are rather shy and tend to hide among water plants or in shaded places. They swim in a jerky manner, letting the tail drop slowly then flicking the fins to bring it up and to let it drop again.

Early in this century the X-ray fish became a favourite aquarium fish, popular not only for its semi-transparency—which was something of a curiosity—but also for its colours and its sprightly movements.

Small but thorough carnivore

The generic name of this fish *Pristella* means 'little saw'. The fish's specific name *riddlei* is in honour of Oscar Riddle who first collected it. Saw-like teeth and an upward-sloping mouth are a clear indication of a carnivorous diet. The X-ray fish is, in fact, closely related to the piranha (p 1777) which has such a bad reputation for savagery. The X-ray fish, being so much smaller, feeds on smaller prey, mainly animal plankton and insect larvae, but it will take anything living of appropriate size, and also small worms. Even when young it feeds on animals such as rotifers, the nauplius larvae of crustaceans, small insect larvae, very small worms and the hosts of microscopic protistans, which used to be known as infusorians, living in the freshwater plankton.

Small fry keep to cover

The female is the more robust, the male being markedly slimmer. The sexes can be told apart by viewing them against the light: the hind end of the body cavity of the female is rounded, while that of the male tapers to a point. In spawning the eggs and milt are shed into the water, fertilisation being external. Each female lays 70—150 eggs at a time. As a rule, spawning takes place in full sunlight, in the morning, among water plants. The eggs hatch in 20—28 hours, the larvae hanging like minute glass rods on the leaves of the water plants for a day or two, before starting to swim. They keep to the cover of vegetation, however, for the first two weeks. They grow rapidly and develop their full colours in about six weeks.

△ *X-ray fish quartet; males escort a female (top).*

Fear of infanticide

There is little precise information on the natural enemies of the X-ray fish, but we can be fairly sure, from the relatively small number of eggs laid, that the number of enemies is small. Indeed, from what is known by keeping these fishes in aquaria the likelihood is that the main dangers are in early infancy and from being eaten by adults of their own kind. Care has to be taken to remove the parents to another tank after they have spawned.

Popular curiosities

It is always of interest to speculate about the reasons why this or that aquarium fish is popular. X-ray fish are colourful and lively but when they were first displayed in the Aquarium of the London Zoo, in the early years of this century, the comments made by visitors suggested it was first and foremost their transparency that captured attention. This may have been because people could see inside a fish—see its internal works—which is not possible with more familiar fishes. There is, however, another possibility—that what they could see was aesthetically pleasing. An X-ray picture of quite an ordinary small fish can be most pleasing to look at. So is a fossil fish in which the skeleton is whole and laid out as an etching in a rock, showing the orderly arrangement of the vertebrae and the ribs.

class	**Pisces**
order	**Cypriniformes**
family	**Characidae**
genus & species	***Pristella riddlei***

Yak

The yak is the wild and also the domestic ox of the Tibetan plateau, and of all large animals it lives in probably the most inhospitable region in the world. The wonder is it can subsist on such scant vegetation. A wild yak is possibly the largest of the cattle tribe; bulls are said to stand 6 ft 8 in. high and to weigh $\frac{3}{4}$ ton. Domestic yak are very much smaller. The shoulders are humped, and there is a long fringe of hair on the shoulders, flanks, thighs and tail, almost sweeping the ground. The coat is black in wild yaks. In the domestic form it varies from black to piebald or white, and the hair is usually longer. Yak have long, thin angular horns, which point straight out sideways, then turn up, and at the tips turn back and inwards. In some domestic yak they turn outwards. The horns sometimes reach over 3 ft in length.

Domestic yak are found all over the highlands of central Asia, from the Rupshu plateau in Ladakh across Tibet to Szechwan, in the Pamir, Tienshan and Altai ranges. Sometimes they are crossed with domestic oxen to give a creature called the zo which is bred mainly in Ladakh and at lower altitudes and is difficult to distinguish from the true yak. Polled yak have been bred in places and zo, too, may be hornless. Wild yak are confined to the highest altitude zones in Tibet and Szechwan, going up to 20 000 ft, which is as high as any mammal in the world lives. They may have been displaced from some areas by domestic yak which compete for the same food, but herdsmen regard them as useful for improving the domestic stock from time to time.

Swinging kilts

The cows and calves of wild yak live for most of the year in herds of 20 – 200. The adult bulls are solitary, or live in herds of up to five. The herds increase in size in the spring, when the freshly sprouting grass attracts large aggregations. In the summer they move higher up the mountains, returning to the lower plateaux in the autumn, where they wade through waterlogged valleys in search of moorland grasses. When the snow comes, around September in Szechwan, they make their way once more to the high ground, and here they wander along the snowy upland moors, on the Roof of the World, in temperatures that may be as low as $-40°C/-40°F$. The herd moves through the snow in single file, each animal placing its feet in the tracks of the one in front. When disturbed, the herd flees at a gallop, their long flank-fringes swaying from side to side, like kilts. Their only predators are wolves and bears, and only an unprotected calf will fall victim even to these.

▷ *Despite its cumbersome appearance, the domestic yak is very sure-footed and an expert climber, sometimes going as high as 20 000 ft.*

roebild

From one extreme to another

Although yak are one of the most cold-adapted animals in the world, they have been kept successfully in the subtropical environment of the Rio de Janeiro zoo, with its summer temperatures of 40°C/104°F. In this climate, the yak grow shorter coats, and their respiratory rate increases.

Clash of foreheads

Yak herds begin to split up in the rut, which takes place in July in Szechwan, but rather earlier in Ladakh. The big bulls fight for possession of cows, pushing against each other with their foreheads but doing no real damage. Gestation lasts for 280 days, so the young are born in April or May.

Economical yak

The economy of the peoples of the Central Asian mountains depends on the domesticated yak, both as a beast of burden and as a milk-producer. The strict lamaistic form of Buddhism practised in Tibet forbids their killing under normal circumstances, although sick yak may be slaughtered humanely. Yak skins are used as cloaks and for tents and rancid yak butter is made into ghee, an oil-like butter. The main use of the yak, however, is as a pack animal. Pure yak are used in the highlands, but at lower altitudes zo are used to carry trade goods, between Ladakh and Kashmir, for example.

Wild yak compete with domestic yak for grazing, but with man on their side the domestic animals always win and wild yak have been driven into the highest and most inaccessible places. In the 14th century wild yak occurred in the Tuva chain. In the 17th, they were known in Kusnezk; in 1739 there were 'not a few' in the Altai and Dauriya, as well as in the Semipalantinsk area. The northern yak—probably ancestral to the domestic yak still used in the southern Altai—have been described as a separate species, *Bos baicalensis.*

Herwart Bohlken has made a special study of wild and domestic cattle. He has pointed out that domestic animals are so variable that to call them by any scientific species name is meaningless. Thus, although Linnaeus in 1758 called the yak *Bos grunniens* (because it grunts rather than moos), domestic yak are so variable that they cannot be classified into a subspecies or race—they have been bred by man and 'sheltered from the environment'—and Bohlken prefers to call the yak *Bos mutus* (a name first given to the wild form), distinguishing the domesticated form just as *Bos mutus forma domestica grunniens* to show from what wild species the domestic yak was derived. He applies similar rules to other wild and domestic cattle, and his point of view is gaining ground.

class	**Mammalia**
order	**Artiodactyla**
family	**Bovidae**
genus & species	***Bos mutus** wild* ***B. mutus** (grunniens) domestic*

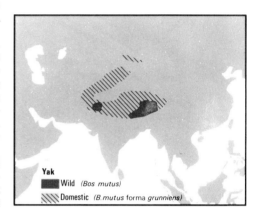

Yak
▮ Wild *(Bos mutus)*
▨ Domestic *(B. mutus forma grunniens)*

At a height of 16 000 ft in Nepal, these yaks are indispensable to the mountain people as beasts of burden and providers of meat, milk and wool.

Yellow-eyed penguin

The yellow-eyed or grand penguin provides a contrast in many respects to the other penguins in this encyclopedia. Of the 17 penguin species only six breed in the Antarctic and only the Adélie (p 15) and the emperor (p 723) are completely confined to the Antarctic, while the king penguin (p 1233) reaches only the fringes. Although the Antarctic is usually thought of as the 'home' of penguins, the remaining 11 species breed around the shores of Africa, Australia and South America reaching as far north as the Galapagos Islands on the equator. The yellow-eyed penguin breeds on the coast of South Island, New Zealand and on Stewart, Auckland and Campbell Islands. In marked contrast to the Antarctic penguins its nests are well scattered among thick vegetation.

The yellow-eyed penguin is medium-sized, about 30 in. long and, like many penguins, has yellow plumes on the head. The plumes of the yellow-eyed penguin are only moderately elongated, unlike the flowing head-dresses of the macaroni and royal penguins. The crown and nape are yellowish gold with black flecks and there is a yellow band running around the head from each yellow eye. The rest of the body is slate grey with white underparts and white edges to the flippers.

Studied for 18 years

The yellow-eyed penguin is distinguished by being the first seabird to have its breeding habits intensively studied. Long-term studies have now been made on many birds but few cover as long a period as that of the yellow-eyed penguin, which was started in 1936 and finished in 1953. Furthermore, it was carried out by an amateur ornithologist, LE Richdale, who worked alone in his spare time. His study was made on a small colony, averaging about 40 nests, in which all the penguins were marked with individually numbered metal rings so that their breeding success, marital faithfulness, and many other aspects of their social life could be studied.

Unlike the Antarctic penguins but like many of those living in warmer waters, yellow-eyed penguins do not migrate. They stay in shallow coastal waters near the breeding places all the year round, coming on shore to roost. They also moult ashore just after the breeding season, the non-breeding penguins doing so first. The latter have to build up reserves of fat after the breeding period to survive the 3-week moulting period, during which they lose 40% of their body weight.

Like other penguins, yellow-eyed penguins feed on small fish and squid.

Nests in holes

We usually think of penguins nesting in dense colonies on bare rocky cliffs and shores but some nest in burrows or crevices. The yellow-eyed penguin nests in holes, among rocks or under fallen logs in thick

Bathing belle, penguin style: a yellow-eyed penguin poses on one of its cliffside haunts.

MF Soper

scrub or forests, up to half a mile from the sea. The nests are well spaced out and one nest may be 100 yd or more from its neighbours. This is in marked contrast to the colonies of the Adélie penguin where it has been found that more chicks are reared in the middle of large colonies where the nests are packed closely together. The advantage of having nests more spaced out is that there is less fighting between neighbours. Nevertheless, there is still some fighting in a colony of yellow-eyed penguins, particularly among young birds establishing nest sites.

The clutch of two white eggs is laid on a nest of sticks and grasses. Most clutches are started in the third week of September and are incubated by both parents for 6–7 weeks. The chicks are then fed at the nest for another 14–16 weeks until they have fledged. This is a long period compared with the 9-week fledging period of the similar-sized Adélie penguin. When they leave their nests, the young penguins, which can be distinguished only by the yellow bands on the sides of the head, gather on pathways leading down to the sea, and take to the water together.

Some yellow-eyed penguins breed when two years old, others wait until they are three. In Richdale's colony 5 out of the 36 penguins lived for more than 18 years.

Low divorce rate

Richdale's study on the yellow-eyed penguin was one of the first to show that some birds return to the same nest site and partner year after year. This is particularly marked in seabirds which are generally long-lived. The 'divorce rate' each year among the yellow-eyed penguins was about 14%, excluding pairs which dissolved through the death of one member, and one pair remained faithful for 13 seasons. A similar divorce rate exists in Adélie penguins and it has been found that two birds are less likely to remate if they were unsuccessful in breeding in the previous season. In other birds the divorce rate may be lower: 2–3%, for instance, in skuas.

In the Adélie penguin it has been shown that there is more to faithfulness to a mate than just two birds returning to their old nest site. Individuals can definitely recognise each other by voice, if not by sight.

class	**Aves**
order	**Sphenisciformes**
family	**Spheniscidae**
genus & species	***Megadyptes antipodes***

Yucca moth

*There is a genus of small American moths
which pollinate the flowers of yucca plants
and whose larvae feed on their seeds. The
mutually dependent relationship between
moth and plant is unusually intricate and
precise. It is, in fact, one of the most
wonderful cases known of balanced symbio-
sis, an association of two wholly distinct
organisms for their mutual advantage.
The larvae of the moth can feed only on
developing seeds of yucca and the plant is
pollinated only by this particular moth.
The moth provides for the needs of both
the plant and her offspring by what appears
to be a deliberate and calculated course of
action on her part.*

*The yucca plants themselves are peculiar.
They grow in Mexico and the southwest
United States and are sometimes called
Spanish bayonets, from the cluster of dark
green sword-like leaves that spring from
the rootstock. A tall stem bearing the
flowers rises from out of the centre of the
clump of leaves. The yucca is a popular
plant in ornamental gardens in Europe as
well as North America.*

*The moths belong to the genus **Tegeticula** (formerly called **Pronuba**) and are
known as yucca moths. They are small white
moths, just under $\frac{1}{2}$ in. long and about
1 in. across the spread wings. The best
known species is **Tegeticula yuccasella**.
Each of the different species is attached
to one particular kind of yucca plant.
Thus, **T. yuccasella** pollinates and feeds
on **Yucca filamentos**, while **Yucca
brevifolia** and **Y. whipplei** are
associated with **Tegeticula synthetica**
and **T. maculata** respectively. The
association was first discovered and
described by the American entomologist
CV Riley in 1872.*

AB Klots

◁ *A mutual dependence: the yucca moth
Tegeticula yuccasella for food from the plant,
the yucca flower for pollination by the insect.*

Precision pollination

The yucca moth becomes active after dark and when she has mated the female seeks out yucca flowers to collect pollen from them. To do this she uses a pair of curved tentacles which are formed from the modified right and left halves of the proboscis; the adult moth never feeds and has no use for a proboscis of the normal type. The pollen is sticky and the moth gathers it from open anthers and works it into a ball, which may be larger than her own head. Holding the ball with her tentacles, head and forelegs, she flies to another flower of the same species and presses the ball of pollen down onto the receptive end or stigma of the female part of the flower. The moth then lays one or two eggs in the ovary, at the base of the style. She may repeat this half-a-dozen times in a single flower. Then she flies off to repeat the process with other flowers. The pollen fertilises the ovules, which develop into seeds on which the larvae feed. As more seeds are produced than the larvae need, some ripen and grow into new yucca plants.

The moth is able to carry out this remarkable operation because of two unusual structural features. One is the modification of the mouth parts already mentioned. The other is the possession by the female of a piercing ovipositor, a most unusual thing among moths.

Insects and flowers

Flowering plants and insects have been evolving side by side since the Cretaceous period, about 100 million years ago, when dinosaurs still walked the earth. We admire the beautiful forms and colours of flowers, and their sweet scent, but they were not evolved for our appreciation. They are for the insects, as is the pollen. Probing into the flowers and flying from one to another the insects become dusted with pollen, so promoting the cross-fertilisation of one plant by another. This is insect pollination at its simplest level, but precise and peculiar adaptations of flowers to secure pollination with greater certainty are quite frequent. Adaptations on the part of the insect, as with the transformation of the yucca moth's proboscis, are more rare. Usually it is no more than a simple lengthening of the proboscis to reach into tubular flowers, best seen in some of the hawk moths.

Orchids show some of the remarkable instances of insects and flowers linked for survival. The pollen of many orchids is concentrated on small club-shaped organs called pollinia. When an insect visits a flower and pokes its head inside, these become detached and stick firmly to the insect's head or proboscis in such a way that when the insect goes to the next flower the pollen on them is applied accurately to the stigma and the flower is fertilised. A few kinds of orchid have, moreover, abandoned the traditional lure of an offer of nectar and they appeal to the insect in another way. In certain small wasps, for example, the males hatch some time before the females, so they hunt in vain for a mate during the earlier period of their adult life. The flower of the orchid concerned in the association has come to resemble the female wasp so closely that the frustrated males actually try to mate with the flowers and in doing so pollinate them. The European fly orchis, *Ophrys insectifera*, is pollinated in this way, but there are other examples of this kind of close relationship between a particular species of orchid and a particular species of wasp. If anything, the association between the yucca moth and the yucca plant is even closer, so if the moth became extinct the yucca plant would be doomed, and vice versa.

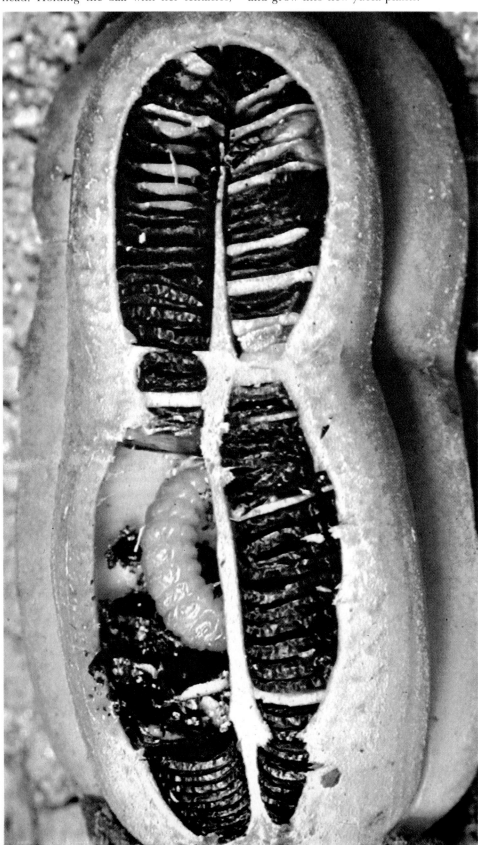

AB Klots

phylum	**Arthropoda**
order	**Lepidoptera**
family	**Prodoxidae**

◁ *Inside the ovary of the yucca flower a yucca moth larva* **Tegeticula yuccasella** *feeds on the flat seeds. As the moth lays only one or two eggs in each seed pod the developing larvae do not eat all the seeds but leave some untouched to start new yucca plants.*

Zambezi shark

This is a shark with many aliases, remarkable for living in fresh water temporarily or permanently. In South Africa it is the Zambezi, shovelnose grey, slipway grey or van Rooyen's shark. In Australia the same species is called the whaler shark. In Central America we meet it again as the Lake Nicaragua shark. In the United States it is the bull, cub or ground shark.

The Zambezi shark has a broad head with a short rounded snout and small eyes. The body is heavy with a prominent triangular first dorsal fin and a small second dorsal fin set well back towards the tail fin with its long upper lobe. The pectoral fins are relatively large. The teeth are triangular with saw edges. The back and flanks are light to dark grey, the underside white. The Zambezi shark is up to 10 ft long and over 400 lb weight. Its distribution is probably worldwide in tropical and subtropical waters.

Attacks on bathers and canoes

This shark normally moves fairly slowly but can suddenly put on speed to attack. It frequents inshore waters and enters estuaries and rivers. Individuals have been caught 300 miles up the Zambezi. In America, as the bull or cub shark, it is also known to go more than 100 miles up rivers. In Central America, Lake Nicaragua, 96 miles long by 30 miles across and 106 ft above sea-level, has a permanent freshwater population. Wherever they are they have a reputation for being aggressive, attacking large fish including other sharks, human bathers and even attacking boats. There are several records of canoes being persistently bumped in the Limpopo River and of one shark biting through the fabric of a canoe so that it eventually sank. There seems to be a connection between the shark's attacks and the presence of fresh water. Off the Natal coast it has been noticed that when floodwaters from rivers are pouring into the sea, bathers in the less salt water have been attacked. There seems to be a greater incidence of attack on bathers in the freshwater Lake Nicaragua than in coastal waters.

In the United States, this shark has the additional common name of 'ground shark'. It has, however, been found in saltwater aquaria, such as the one at Durban, that unless it is injured or diseased, the Zambezi shark does not lie on the bottom. If it does it soon dies from lack of oxygen. Normally the shark swims continuously round and round the tank, night and day. Sharks cannot pump water across the gills, as bony fishes do, but must keep on the move to maintain the flow of water.

Cat-like vision

Sharks traditionally find their human victims by smell, especially following blood trails in the water. They must use sight as well, and this is emphasized by the accounts of persistent and seemingly deliberate attacks on boats. Although the eyes of the Zambezi shark are small we can assess its sight by studies made on related species in the same family. These show the eye to be well adapted for vision in bright and dim light. The retina is rich in rods but poor in cones, indicating a high degree of visual sensitivity, poor colour vision and poor discrimination of detail. A canoe would, therefore, be merely a fish-like shape, and one to be attacked. Another feature of the shark's eye is the tapetum lucidum, a layer of silvered, mirror-like plates which reflects light rays back through the retina so that the shark, like the cat on land, can make full use of light of low intensity. As with cats,

△ *Dappled by sunlight, a Zambezi shark and attached remora in a research tank at Durban.*

the pupil is a vertical slit in bright light but round and well open in subdued light.

Although it attacks other objects, including bathers, the real food of the Zambezi shark is other fishes, especially rays and other sharks.

Breeds in fresh water?

It is noticeable that the Zambezi shark enters the St Lucia estuary in Natal in large numbers during November and December. It is assumed they go into brackish or fresh water to give birth to their live young. The small immature sharks are the ones found farthest upstream leaping from the water in estuaries. It is even possible that, for the shark, fresh water is linked with breeding, which is a time when many animals are at their most aggressive.

Killer whales the enemy

Tests on several sharks, including the Zambezi shark have shown that they respond to sounds over a wide frequency and are able to determine the direction of the sounds. The sharks were conditioned, in the time honoured way, to associate sounds with food. Then an interesting experiment was carried out with a tape recording of the sounds made by a group of killer whales 600 yd away. When these high pitched sounds were transmitted into the Shark Research Tank at Durban all the sharks in the tank were unmoved by them except for a large Zambezi shark. This seemed to be agitated and swam rapidly round and round the tank. The killer whale is the most powerful predator in the sea and this experiment could be taken to mean that the Zambezi shark is one of its habitual victims.

Prosecutor's evidence

In the last 10 years or so several books have been written on the clinical side of shark attack. It is clear from these that all too often the identity of the shark that has lacerated a human bather is in doubt. The attack is sudden, the attacker is underwater with at most a small part of the fin showing, and usually competent observers are not present who might name the shark with certainty. The teeth of the Zambezi shark have been described as flattened blades with saw edges made on the same principle as a steak knife. They are, however, liable to break on contact with bone and the victim takes with him fragments of teeth in his wounds, usually embedded in the bones, that effectively name the villain of the piece.

class	Selachii
order	Pleurotremata
family	Carcharhinidae
genus & species	*Carcharhinus leucas*

Zebra

Zebras are distinguished from horses and asses by the stripes on their bodies. Their mane is neat and upright. The tail is tufted as in asses, but the hard wart-like knobs known as 'chestnuts', are found on the forelegs only, and not on the hindlegs as in horses. There are differences from both the horse and the ass in the skull and teeth. Three species of zebra live in Africa today. The commonest and best-known is Burchell's zebra, which extends from Zululand in the southeast, and from Etosha Pan in southwest Africa, north as far as southern Somalia and southern Sudan. In this species the stripes reach under the belly, and on the flanks they broaden and bend backwards towards the rump, forming a Y-shaped 'saddle' pattern. Although the races in the southern and northern parts of the range look quite different, the differences are only clinal. That is, there are gradual changes from south to north, but they all belong to one species. In the southernmost race, the 'true' Burchell's zebra, now extinct but once living in the Orange Free State and neighbouring areas, the ground colour was yellowish rather than white; the legs were white and unstriped; the stripes often did not reach under the belly; and between the broad main stripes of the hindquarters and neck were lighter, smudge-grey alternating stripes commonly known as 'shadow-stripes'.

Further north a race known as Chapman's zebra is still found. It has a lighter ground colour than the true Burchell's, the stripes reach further down the legs — usually to below the knees — and the shadow-stripes are still present. All zebras still living from Zululand north to the Zambezi are referred to as members of this race; but at Etosha Pan there are some zebras that have almost no leg stripes and closely resemble 'true' Burchell's.

North of the Zambezi is the East African race, known as Grant's zebra. Its ground colour is white, the stripes continue all the way down to the hoofs and there are rarely any shadow-stripes. Grant's zebra is smaller than the southern races, about 50 in. high, weighs 500—600 lb, and has a smaller

mane. In the northern districts the mane has disappeared altogether. Maneless zebras occur in southern Sudan, the Karamoja district of Uganda and the Juba valley of Somalia.

South and southwest of the Burchell's zebras' range lives the mountain zebra, about the same size as Burchell's but with a prominent dewlap halfway between the jaw angle and the forelegs. Its stripes always stop short of the white belly. Its ground colour is whitish and, although the stripes on the flanks bend back to the rump, as in Burchell's, the vertical bands continue as well, giving a 'grid iron' effect. The southern race, the stockily built, broad-banded Cape mountain zebra, is nearly extinct, preserved only on a few private properties. The race in southwest Africa, Hartmann's zebra, is still fairly common. It is larger and longer-limbed than the Cape mountain zebra, with narrower stripes and a buff ground colour.

The third species is Grévy's zebra, from Somalia, eastern Ethiopia and northern Kenya, a very striking, tall zebra. The belly is white and unstriped, and there are no stripes on the hindquarters, except the dorsal stripe which bisects it. On the haunches the stripes from the flanks, rump and hindlegs seem to bend towards each other and join up.

▽ At the waterhole: a herd of southeast African Burchell's zebra. This race generally has striped legs and a paler ground colour than the now extinct true Burchell's zebra.

Belligerent stallions

Burchell's zebras are strongly gregarious. Groups of 1–6 mares with their foals keep together under the leadership of a stallion, who protects them and also wards off other stallions. Sometimes, for no apparent reason, the male simply disappears and another one takes his place. The surplus stallions live singly, or in bachelor groups of up to 15 members. Burchell's zebras are rather tame, not showing as much fear of man as the gnu with which they associate. When alarmed they utter their barking alarm call, a hoarse 'kwa-ha, kwa-ha', ending with a whinny. Then the herd wheels off, following the gnu. When cornered, however, the herd stallion puts up a stiff resistance, kicking and biting.

Mountain zebras, said to be more savage than Burchell's, live in herds of up to six, although sometimes they assemble in large numbers where food is plentiful. They seem to have regular paths over the rugged hills and move along them in single file. The call of the mountain zebra has been described as a low, snuffling whinny, quite different from that of the Burchell's.

Although in Grévy's zebra there are family groups as well as bachelor herds, the biggest and strongest stallions, weighing up to 1 000 lb, are solitary, each occupying a territory of about a mile in diameter.

Slow breeding rate

A newborn foal has brown stripes and is short-bodied and high-legged like the foal of a domestic horse. It is born after a gestation of 370 days. It weighs 66–77 lb and stands about 33 in. high. The mares come into season again a few days after foaling, but only 15% are fertilised a second time; usually a mare has one foal every three years. They reach sexual maturity at a little over 1 year, but do not seem to be fertile before about 2 years. Young males leave the herd between 1 and 3 years and join the bachelor herd. At 5 or 6 years many of them attempt to kidnap young females and if successful a new one-male herd is formed. The unsuccessful ones remain in the bachelor herd, or become solitary. Zebras live as long as horses, 29 years being the record.

Lions beware

Man still hunts the zebra for meat but in protected areas, at least, very little of this continues. The zebra, with the gnu, is the lion's favourite prey. Because zebras are potentially dangerous, the lion must make a swift kill and young lions have been routed by zebra stallions that turned on them. Astley Maberley tells the story of an African poacher who was killed and fearfully mangled by an irate troop of Burchell's zebras after he had killed a foal.

(1) Linear line-up: a row of Grévy's zebra, large, handsomely-marked animals recognised by the huge ears and narrowly-spaced stripes.
(2) Topi antelope and Grant's zebra—a species having stripes that reach below the knees. The odd-looking animal on the left of the picture is a rare melanistic form of Grant's zebra.
(3) Grant's zebra spar in the dust of Ngorongoro crater. Zebra stallions are aggressive not only to males of the same species but also to predators, including man.

1

H Klingel
2

4

Sally Anne Thompson

3
5

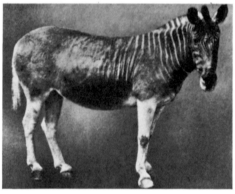

The lost quagga

A fourth species of zebra, the quagga, was extremely common in South Africa 150 years ago. It has since been completely exterminated. Most closely resembling Burchell's zebra, the quagga was distinctly striped brown and off-white on the head and neck only. Along the flanks the stripes gradually faded out to a plain brown, sometimes extending to just behind the shoulders, sometimes reaching the haunches. The legs and belly were white. Its barking, high-pitched cry, after which it was named, was rather like that of the Burchell's zebra.

The early explorers, around 1750–1800, met quaggas as far southwest as the Swellendam and Ceres districts, a short way inland from Cape Town. The Boer farmers did not appreciate quaggas except as food for their Hottentot servants. Their method of hunting was to take a train of wagons out onto the veldt and blaze away at everything within sight. Then large numbers of carcases would be loaded onto the wagons, and the rest of the dead and dying animals were simply left to rot. It is no wonder that today Cape Province is virtually denuded of wild game. When Cape Province was emptied, the trekkers to the Orange Free State repeated the process there. By 1820 the quaggas' range was already severely curtailed; they were almost gone even from the broad plains of the Great Fish River, which had been named 'Quagga's Flats' from the vast numbers of them roaming there. A few lingered for another 20 years or so in the far east of Cape Province and in the Orange Free State, the last wild ones being shot near Aberdeen, CP, in 1858, and near Kingwilliamstown in 1861. Strange to say, no one realised that they were even endangered. Zoos looking for replacements for their quaggas that had died were quite shocked to be told, 'But there aren't any more'.

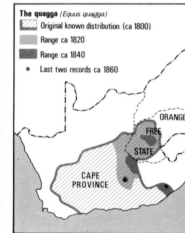

The quagga (*Equus quagga*)
- Original known distribution (ca 1800)
- Range ca 1820
- Range ca 1840
- * Last two records ca 1860

ORANGE FREE STATE

CAPE PROVINCE

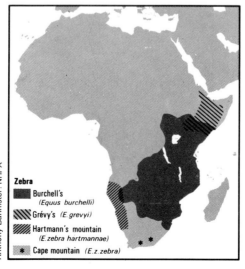

Zebra
- Burchell's (*Equus burchelli*)
- Grévy's (*E.grevyi*)
- Hartmann's mountain (*E.zebra hartmannae*)
- * Cape mountain (*E.z.zebra*)

class	**Mammalia**
order	**Perissodactyla**
family	**Equidae**
genus & species	***Equus burchelli burchelli*** *true Burchell's zebra or bontequagga*
	E. b. antiquorum *Chapman's or southeast African Burchell's*
	E. b. boehmi *Grant's or East African Burchell's*
	E. b. borensis *maneless zebra*
	E. grevyi *Grévy's zebra*
	E. quagga *quagga*
	E. zebra zebra *Cape mountain zebra*
	E. z. hartmannae *Hartmann's mountain zebra*

(4) '. . . along a mountain track' – Hartmann's mountain zebra, a recently described race of the Cape mountain zebra, has a large dewlap between chin and forelegs and stripes that end short of the belly. The stripes form a 'gridiron' effect on the rump.
(5) Nearly extinct: less than 200 Cape mountain zebra live in specially protected areas of high tableland in western Cape province.
(6) Extinct: the quagga was hunted in large numbers by early white settlers to South Africa.

1 Birth of a Grant's zebra: disturbed by a rhinoceros, a female zebra in labour canters off to find a more private place.

2 More of the birth sac exposed: the mare rears her head at the emergence of the foal's front legs—the head appears minutes later.

3 The foal's birth is completed after only 7 minutes. The mare, exhausted after the ordeal, lies back in the grass to rest.

4 The foal is the first to move: after only a few seconds in the outside world, it shakes its head and tries to free itself from the sac.

5 The foal twists and turns to break the
umbilical cord, then in a surge of movement,
struggles hard to stand up on shaky legs.

6 Mother proudly watches foal's progress: like
a skier's first trip on the slopes, the foal
discovers that standing is no easy matter.

7 After its energetic antics the foal needs
nourishment; maternal instinct tells the zebra
her foal is hungry and she gets up to feed it.

8 A guarded escort: the young foal stays close
to its mother's flanks as they trot off to
rejoin the herd in safer pastures.

Zebra finch

In the wild the zebra finch is found only in Australia but it has become very well-known in many countries as a favourite cage bird. It is small, compact and like most finches, is about $3\frac{1}{2}-4\frac{1}{2}$ in. long. The male is more brightly coloured than the female. His back and wings are a light brownish-grey, the crown a dark grey and the sides of the neck and throat are grey finely barred with black, with a black area on the crop. There are distinctive orange or chestnut cheek patches separated from the white feathers round the base of the beak by a black stripe. The flanks are light chestnut spotted with white and the underparts are white. The tail is black with broad white bars and the strong beak and legs are a bright orange-red. The female lacks the male's bright cheek patches and white-spotted chestnut sides as well as his black mark and barrings on the throat. Her underparts have a buffish tinge. A number of colour variations or mutations have, however, been bred in the cage bird.

The zebra is the most common of the Australian finches being found throughout the continent except for the wet coastal forest areas.

Flocking together

The wild zebra finch lives in the grasslands and savannah woodlands. It is an active and hardy little bird that lives in flocks which wander about from place to place in search of food. It is remarkably unafraid of man. Although zebra finches have a variety of calls they are not song birds. They call to each other with a soft low *tet-tet* which can be heard all the time the flock is moving about. The identity call is louder and sounds rather like the note from a small toy trumpet. When aggressive or chasing another bird zebra finches have a special attacking call which resembles the sound of the sudden tearing of a piece of cloth.

A zebra finch will never roost on the branch of a tree if it can find some sort of nest. Sometimes simple untidy nests are made for roosting, often without a roof, or else old breeding nests are renovated.

Mainly seed-eater

The zebra finch feeds on or near the ground chiefly on grass seeds which are either picked up from the ground or pulled from the stem. During the breeding season it supplements its diet with small insects taken from the ground or caught in flight.

Prolific breeder

The zebra finch breeds at almost any time of the year except in the middle of winter. It may build its own nest in a thick prickly bush or in a tree as high as 30 ft from the ground, or it may use holes of various kinds, old nests of other birds or even a rabbit burrow. It may even lay its eggs under the large stick-nests of birds of prey. If it builds its own nest, it constructs an untidy affair of grasses or small twigs and roots, lined with feathers, plant down and wool. Both male and female build the nest, incubate the eggs and feed the nestlings. From 3 to 7 usually 4 or 5, white eggs are laid. Occasionally more than one hen will lay in the same nest and 23 eggs have been recorded in one nest at Marble Bar. The young birds hatch out in $12\frac{1}{2}-14$ days and are fed in the nest for $9-12$ days on half-ripe and ripe grass seeds regurgitated from the parents' crops. They leave the nest on about the 14th day but the parents continue to feed them for another two weeks, and during this time they usually spend the night in the nest. The fledglings resemble the female in colouring but the bill is black until $8-11$ weeks of age when it changes to the adult's orange-red. Sexual maturity is reached when it is about three months old.

Favourite cage bird

The zebra finch is one of the commonest of all cage and aviary birds and one of the easiest to keep and breed in captivity. Although there is now a ban on the export of these birds from Australia most breeders had already established reliable strains before the ban was imposed so it is of little disadvantage. A number of colour variations have been bred in which the normal grey of the body and wings is replaced by another colour as for example in the silver zebra finch and the fawn zebra finch. The white zebra finch is white except for the beak and legs and the sexes look almost identical.

A number of these hardy and gregarious birds can be kept together in an outdoor aviary all the year round so long as dry, draught-proof sleeping quarters are provided with perhaps a little heat in the winter months. Breeding birds are, however, best housed in an indoor aviary. Feeding is no problem as the birds will thrive on millet and canary seeds with some fresh green food. Water and grit and some form of shell-forming substance are also needed.

The zebra finch is the easiest and most prolific breeder in captivity of any of the finches and given the opportunity would breed nonstop throughout the year. Too many clutches, however, weaken the hen and produce less healthy chicks. Whether it is the result of the easy living conditions of being kept in captivity, or because of a natural urge to break records, some zebra finches have a misguided habit of laying one clutch of eggs, covering it with nesting material and then laying another clutch on top. The effort is wasted, however, because none of the eggs hatches.

$\triangledown$ *Ruling the roost: a male zebra finch is put firmly in his place by his mate — the top bird.*

class	**Aves**
order	**Passeriformes**
family	**Fringillidae**
genus & species	***Taeniopygia castanotis***

Barnaby's

Zebra fish

There are several fishes with a common name that includes the word 'zebra'. The most noticeable of these is a small fresh-water fish of Bengal and eastern India. Less than 2 in. long, it is called the zebra fish or zebra danio and is a member of the large carp family. It is an extremely popular fish with aquarists.

It is a slim fish with the body only slightly compressed. The single dorsal fin and the anal fins are fairly large, and it has a relatively large tailfin and small pelvic and pectoral fins. There are two pairs of barbels. The back is brownish-olive, the belly yellowish-white and the flanks are Prussian blue with four golden stripes from the gill cover to the base of the tail. The dorsal fin is also blue with yellow at its base and a white tip. The anal fin is again blue-gold barred, and so is the tailfin. The effect of the stripes is to make the fish look even more streamlined than it is, and to give an impression of movement even when the fish is stationary.

Beauty in repetition

As so often happens with a fish of outstanding colour, subsequently popular with aquarists, there is little that is zoologically striking in zebra fishes. They swim among water plants or in schools—it is when they are all aligned, swimming in formation, evenly spaced, and all travelling in the same direction that they most catch the eye. Almost certainly their attraction owes much to the repetition of their stripes—termed the 'beauty in repetition' by Dr Dilwyn John in 1947. In 1935, William T Innes came very near to saying this in his comprehensive book *Exotic Aquarium Fishes* when he described it as a fish 'to show to advantage moving in schools, it scarcely has an equal, for its beautiful horizontal stripes, repeated in each fish, give a streamline effect that might well be the envy of our best automobile designers'.

Thwarting the egg-eaters

Zebra fishes are carnivorous, feeding on any small animals they can swallow, which usually means small insect larvae, crustaceans and worms. After their colour, their strongly carnivorous tendencies provide one of their more interesting features. They are egg-eaters, and those who breed zebra fish in aquaria need to take special precautions to achieve success.

There is little difference between the sexes except that the female, especially just before spawning, is more plump than the male, and her stripes are more silver and yellow than the golden stripes of the male. In the pre-spawning behaviour the male leads the female in among the water plants and the two take up position side by side, she to shed her ova, he to shed his milt over them to fertilise them. As the eggs slowly sink there is a tendency for the two to snap up the eggs. The first precaution for the aquarist is therefore to provide a breeding aquarium with water so shallow that the

fish have no chance to catch the eggs before they sink to safety in the spaces between the gravel on the bottom. The correct size of gravel pebbles must be used or the adults may become trapped between them. Marbles have been used, or else some sort of trap. An early trap used was a series of slender glass rods held together at the ends with soft wire and raised just off the bottom of the aquarium. This was later superseded by fine metal mesh or nylon.

Each female lays about 200 eggs which hatch in two days. The larvae are at first fairly helpless and inactive, but two days later they can swim and start to feed on microscopic plankton animals. They begin to breed at a year old. At two years they are old-aged, and a zebra fish of three or more years old is an extreme rarity.

Question of stripes

The name 'zebra' is from an Amharic or Ethiopian word and first gained currency in Europe in 1600. By the early years of the 19th century its use had been extended not only to cover all manner of striped animals but also materials showing stripes, and especially to striped shawls and scarves. In the world of fishes there is the zebra shark of the Indian Ocean, with black or brown bars on the body, more like the stripes of a tiger. So we have the anomaly of the common name being zebra shark and the scientific name *Stegostoma tigrinum*. In the extreme south of South America is the zebra salmon *Haplochiton zebra*. In pisciculture there is a hybrid of the trout *Salmo trutta* and the American brook trout *Salvelinus fontinalis*, which is called the zebra hybrid. A foot-long marine fish of the Indo-Pacific *Therapon jarbua* is sometimes called the zebra or tiger fish. It is, however, among the aquarium fishes that the name is most used —the striped or zebra barb *Barbus fasciatus* of Malaya and the East Indies is an example. The common killifish *Fundulus heteroclitus*, of North America, is also called the zebra killie, while the zebra cichlid *Cichlasoma nigrofasciatum* is also—and more appropriately—called the convict fish. Some of these fish have horizontal stripes and others vertical, and there has been some disagreement over which are more correctly termed 'zebra'. However, since a glance at a photograph of a zebra shows that the stripes run in different directions on the different areas of the body, there seems no reason why the name should not be applied to all.

class	**Pisces**
order	**Atheriniformes**
family	**Cyprinodontidae**
genus & species	**Brachydanio rerio**

▽ *On the right lines: the popular zebra fish proves that parallel stripes never meet.*

Zebra mouse

The zebra mouse, also known as the striped field mouse or four-striped grass mouse, is found only in Africa. It is slightly larger than a house mouse, with a head and body length of 3½ – 5 in. and a long tail of 3 – 5¼ in. The fur is coarse, the upper parts of the body varying in colour from yellowish-grey to light greyish brown with lighter underparts. There are three light stripes down the middle of the back from the back of the neck to the base of the tail with dark stripes on either side of them. Sometimes there is only one light stripe with one dark stripe on each side. The light stripes vary from pale yellowish grey to buff while the dark stripes may be anything from a golden brown or clay colour to a dark brown or almost black. The tail is scaly, thickly covered with short hairs.

There is only one species of zebra mouse, which ranges from Tanzania, Kenya and Uganda southward to the extreme southern tip of Africa. A second species of similar size, range and habits is sometimes called a zebra rat, but is more often known as the striped grass mouse or single striped field mouse, although it mostly has half a dozen lines of light coloured spots on each side of the body.

Alert and active

Zebra mice are fairly common throughout their range, living in grassy or cultivated areas up to 9 000 ft or more above sea level. Unlike most rats and mice they are active during the day, sheltering during the night in underground burrows, in weed-covered banks or old termite mounds. They are very alert and active, with good eyesight, and although they stay mostly on or under the ground they have occasionally been seen climbing about the low branches of shrubs. When the sun is not too hot they come out and bask.

When taken young these mice make attractive and lively pets, especially as, unlike many rodent pets, they are active in the daytime. Given the right conditions they will readily breed in captivity.

Variety of foods

The main food of the zebra mouse consists of grass, bark, roots, seeds, berries and cultivated grain of various kinds. Zebra mice will also take snails, insects and eggs. In captivity they flourish on a wide variety of food, taking sunflower, canary and millet seeds and fresh melon pips and almost any sort of fruit, including apple, banana, grape and even holly berries.

Born under or above ground

It is thought that the breeding season in the wild is from September to April, with possibly 4 litters a year. The litters are usually small, with 4 or 5 young but there may be up to 7 young and as many as 12 to a litter have been recorded. The babies are usually born in a nest in a burrow but occasionally the female makes the nest above ground in a dense shrub or in a thick tuft of grass. The nest is made of grass, leaves and moss. Like all baby mice they are born naked, blind and helpless, only about 1 in. long, but they are clearly striped at birth, the stripes being marked by dark pigment in the otherwise pink skin. The babies when very young make plaintive, bat-like squeaks. By the third day the eyes open and they begin to groom themselves and a few days later they can stagger about and try to feed on any food left around. By a fortnight old they are lively and active. They are sexually mature at 3 months. Sometimes family groups of 12 – 30 have been seen living in the same nest.

Many enemies

Like all small rodents, zebra mice have many enemies. These include the smaller carnivores such as mongooses, and the medium-sized jackals, but surprisingly also the large predators like the secretary bird, even the cheetah. Hawks will also take them as well as pythons and cobras. The young ones born in nests above ground are especially vulnerable.

Nine miles a week!

Some years ago Mr and Mrs Kim Taylor carried out an interesting experiment with a pair which were housed in a cage large enough to give them plenty of room to run around. A wheel was placed in the cage for the mice to play with. After preliminary hesitations both male and female took to this sort of treadmill and soon were turning it, either separately or together, when the two would stand side by side spinning it in a concerted effort. A meter was then fixed to the wheel to register the number of times the wheel was turned by the mice in a given time. From this it was calculated that in the first ten weeks the mice had turned the wheel a million times, and that this was the equivalent of the pair running, between them, 180 miles. Assuming they shared the wheel equally, this gives the equivalent of 90 miles per mouse in ten weeks, or nine miles a week, which is just about the sort of distance a mouse in the wild would be expected to cover in its search for food.

The interest of the experiment lies in the fact that the pair of mice using the wheel produced two healthy litters totalling nine babies, whereas a pair of zebra mice kept under exactly the same conditions but with no wheel to play on, did not breed at all during the same period of time. It is, perhaps, reasonable to assume that the provision of a wheel in their cage gave the mice not only a greater zest for living, by providing them with recreation, but in doing so contributed something essential to their mental and physical well-being, which a life in captivity otherwise lacks.

class	**Mammalia**
order	**Rodentia**
family	**Muridae**
genus & species	***Rhabdomys pumilio***

Left: inquisitive group of juvenile zebra mice. Below: marathon mouse clocks up another mile.

Jane Burton: Photo Res

Zebu

The zebu or Brahman cattle originated in southern Asia, possibly in India, but their wild ancestor is unknown. The zebu has a prominent hump on the shoulders, which is an enlarged muscle rather than a store of fat as is usually claimed. Its coat is grey but may be white or black, its legs are slender, and its horns are more upright than those of the aurochs, the wild ancestor of European cattle (p 398). It has a marked dewlap and drooping ears. Some scientists claim it was domesticated from the wild gaur or the banteng of south-east Asia, but it differs from these in its long slender face and in other features.

Domestication of the zebu may have been earlier than that of western cattle. The first record was made in 4500 BC, but on seals from West Pakistan, dated 2500 BC, there are representations of both zebu and western cattle. The two kinds readily hybridise and offspring from such crosses have produced some of the breeds found in Africa, where the zebu is better adapted to the hot climate.

Less sweat, more milk

Of recent years much research has been directed towards making more use of such crosses. The western cattle are better for milk production, but this and meat production declines in animals taken from temperate to tropical countries. Zebu are usually better for meat production. The zebu has larger ears than western cattle, and these and its dewlap offer a large surface for loss of body heat by radiation. In other words, zebu can, because of their build, keep cooler than western cattle which, taken to the tropics, spend less time grazing and more time lying in the shade. So they tend to suffer from permanent malnutrition. This is enhanced by their woolly coat, which also inhibits heat loss, so they lose more water through their breathing which, among other things, lowers their milk yield. Modern research is aimed at producing hybrids that combine the most advantageous characters from the two species for giving maximum milk or meat production, or both. The research is intensive, and includes a close study of the sweat-glands of the two species, on the assumption that sweating and milk-production are mutually exclusive. But hybridizing the two has been carried out repeatedly, in different places, in the course of history. The Sanga cattle, widespread in Africa, originated probably in Egypt from crossing Hamitic longhorn cattle with zebu.

▷ *In complete harmony with the scene, a herdsman and his placid zebu cattle amble along a peaceful beach on Nossi Bé, off Madagascar. The economic value of the zebu in Madagascar has been acknowledged on her postage stamps.*

Gerald Cubitt

Okapia

△ *Tolerant zebus plod round a never-ending circle, pumping water to irrigate the surrounding land.*
▽ *Infant inspection; an adult zebu washes a newly-born young while another watches closely.*

Gentle and docile

There is a distinct difference in temperament between the two species of cattle. The zebu is more tractable and docile yet is more lively than western cattle and grunts rather than moos. In walking it swings its hindlegs in a straight line, like a horse, instead of using the sideways movement of the dairy cow. It has endurance and speed, and zebu are recorded as carrying a soldier on their back for 16 hours a day at a speed of 6 mph. Zebus were frequently used for drawing vehicles, from state carriages to heavy farm wagons or ploughs, and are still used today for transporting heavy loads.

W Youatt, writing in 1832, described the zebu as 'very fond of being noticed; and often, when he is lying down, if anyone to whom he is accustomed goes and sits down on him and strokes him over the face, he will turn round and put his head on their lap, and lie there contentedly so long as they please.' Professor John Francis, in *Nature*, 1965, comments that this 'perfectly portrays the temperament of the Brahman'.

Zebu are said to clear a five-barred gate with ease. Youatt tells of a calf which would leap over an iron fence to reach water, and when it had drunk its fill it would leap back again with ease.

Tick- and heat-resistant

The zebu has been taken across the tropical and sub-tropical regions of the Old World, from China to Africa. It was taken to the United States a century ago and also to Australia, especially to Queensland. Its popularity, and that of hybrids with western cattle, in the United States rests not only on its ability to stand up to heat but also on its immunity to ticks that carry Texas fever. The hybrids share this immunity at the same time producing a better meat than the pure zebu.

The size of zebu ranges from that of a small donkey to animals larger than any western cattle. Their horns also show a wide range, from hornless and small-horned, with horns shorter than the ears, to the Ankole cattle of Uganda. The Ankole has enormous swept-back horns, stout and up to 5 feet long.

class	**Mammalia**
order	**Artiodactyla**
family	**Bovidae**
genus & species	***Bos indicus***

Okapia

△ *In practice, Indian cow-worship is restricted to one species: the Indian humped zebu.*
▽ *Reliable zebus with their load dawdle on while the sleeping drivers take advantage.*

Heather Angel

2685

△ *Although it looks like a skunk, the zorille is more closely related to the weasels and polecats.*
▷ *Playful and innocent though he seems, the malodorous zorille is shunned by potential predators.*

Zorille

The zorille, sometimes spelt zorilla, or striped polecat of Africa, bears a strong resemblance to the American striped skunks, although it is only distantly related to them. It is a small slender animal with a head and body length of 11 – 15 in. and a tail 8 – 12 in. long. Its long fur is strikingly marked in black and white. The body is black with broad white stripes down the back, the face is black with three large white spots and the bushy tail is mainly white. Like the skunks, when disturbed, the zorille ejects a strong evil-smelling fluid from its anal glands.

*The zorille is one of the most common mammals of Africa, ranging from Senegal, northern Nigeria, the Sudan and Ethiopia to southern Africa. Although there is only one species many local races have been described. Two slightly smaller relatives of the zorille in Africa resemble it in having black and white markings. They are the Libyan striped weasel **Poecilictis libyca** from North Africa and the white-naped weasel **Poecilogale albinucha** from central South Africa. They are known as snake-weasels either because they kill snakes or because their low flat head is like the head of a puff-adder.*

Evil-smelling defence

The zorille is found in a variety of habitats but it seems to favour dry areas. It is nocturnal and usually solitary except in the breeding season. During the day it shelters in rock crevices or in burrows dug with its long, strong claws. Sometimes it uses the burrows of other animals or even shelters under farm buildings or outhouses. It hunts during the night usually on the ground but if necessary can climb and swim after its prey. It trots slowly along on its short legs with its back slightly hunched, waving its long bushy tail.

At the sight of an enemy the zorille erects the hair on its body and turning its back towards the intruder it stiffly raises its tail. If actually attacked it ejects the fluid from its anal glands and is said to do so with deadly accuracy, usually into the face of the enemy. The fluid is said to be so potent that it is able to blind another animal almost instantly. Sometimes, if its enemy still persists, the zorille will feign death, so often escaping being mauled or killed. There seems to be a difference of opinion about the fluid – some people say it is less pungent than that of the American skunks while others claim its odour is worse than that of any other animal. It is possible that its odour may vary with the age of the individual or perhaps even with the time of year. The people of the Sudan, however, are in no doubt about this for they have named the zorille the 'Father of Stinks'.

Good rodent catcher

The zorille's food consists mainly of mice and other rodents, small reptiles, birds and large insects. It will follow the burrowing mole rats underground to catch and eat them. It will also sometimes take eggs and snakes. Although it may occasionally kill poultry it does more good than harm around farms in keeping down rodents. The food is bolted in lumps rather than chewed, and as with cats it is not held with the paws before being eaten. A habit the zorille shares with other small members of the weasel family is of catching surplus food. It will kill more than it needs for immediate consumption and will pile the carcases in a neat heap.

Gentle pet

Not much is known of the breeding habits of the zorille. The litter size is usually two or three, the young being born in a burrow. If taken young the zorille can make a friendly and gentle pet, seldom emitting its fluid except when frightened or angry. This is common experience with other mustelids, such as the European polecat, that can give out a noxious fluid. A fully tamed individual will discharge the fluid only if suddenly shocked. Zorilles have in the past occasionally been kept in zoos; one lived for over five years in the London Zoo.

Given a wide berth

Although the zorille may occasionally be attacked by dogs or larger predators, most animals, warned by its striking black and white colouring, give it a wide berth to avoid being sprayed by its evil-smelling fluid.

A matter of size

Ivan T Sanderson, in his *Living Mammals of the World*, quotes a famous game warden for the story of how nine fully grown lions were warded off around a freshly killed zebra by a zorille. The zorille had taken possession and for several hours sniffed around the carcase, occasionally nibbling at it, even taking a nap with its back to the zebra. Whenever a lion made an attempt to approach the carcase the zorille raised its tail in warning and the big cats retired, frightened of the stream of amber-coloured liquid that might follow.

This contrasts with the behaviour of the tame white-naped weasel kept by Anne J Alexander and RF Ewer as reported in *African Wild Life* for 1959. These two observers found that their weasels would kill and eat mice. They would also eat the bodies of dead mice. When offered the carcases of a freshly killed pigeon, rabbit or domestic cat, the weasels 'merely sniffed towards the potential prey, then ran away'. The only conclusion they could come to was that it was a question of size.

class	**Mammalia**
order	**Carnivora**
family	**Mustelidae**
genus & species	***Ictonyx striatus***

Zool Soc London

Mixture: with the size and shape of a dog, the grace of a cat and the name of a fox, the zorro is one of the many South American mystery animals.

Zorro

Zorro, the Spanish word for fox, has been applied to several of the South American dogs which are not strictly foxes but are fox-like members of the dog family. The name is best given to the small-eared zorro which does not seem to be closely related to any other member of the dog family. This, together with other aspects, makes it an intriguing animal, even more so because nothing has been recorded of its behaviour and habits in the wild and as yet only a few individuals have been kept in captivity.

The small-eared zorro is so called because its ears are shorter than those of any other dog, domestic breeds excepted. They are $1\frac{1}{4}-2$ in. long, the body being $28-39$ in. with a $10-14$in. tail. The head is large, and the legs short. Apart from the maned wolf (p 1396) the zorro is the largest of the South American dogs, standing about 14 in. at the shoulder. The hair is dark grey to black above and rufous mixed with grey and black underneath. The tail is long and bushy and is carried curled forward with the tip turned up to prevent it sweeping the ground. A peculiar feature of the zorro is the long upper canine teeth which project $\frac{1}{4}$ in. when the mouth is closed.

The range of the zorro, so far as is known, is in tropical America, in the Amazon basin in Brazil, Colombia, Ecuador and Peru, in the Orinoco basin in Colombia and probably Venezuela, and in the Rio Parana basin in Brazil.

Graceful cat-like movement

The zorro's existence was made known to science in 1882 when a live specimen arrived at London Zoo, and knowledge of its habits is virtually limited to observations on a pair kept at Brookfield Zoo, Chicago. When a zorro is excited the hairs of its tail are raised, giving rise to the name of flag-tailed dog. The male at Brookfield became extremely tame, and would wag its tail feebly and roll over on its back, squealing, when petted by people it knew. The female, on the other hand, was unfriendly.

One of the most noticeable features of the zorro's behaviour is the cat-like grace of its movements, quite unlike the plodding, stiff gait of most dogs. It would be interesting to know whether it is cat-like in its behaviour, approaching its prey by stealth rather than by running it down, for instance. The coat is very sleek and it has been suggested that this is related either to a life where there is frequent rain or to a partly aquatic life. With regard to the latter it is of interest that the zorro looks most like a bush dog (p 329), which is said to swim well.

Both the zorro and bush dog have very small ears which is surprising in view of the general rule that extremities become smaller as one goes towards the polar regions; compare, for instance, the ears of the tropical fennec fox and the polar Arctic fox. The reduction in ear size is related to the need to conserve heat by cutting down on the surface area of the body. It may be that the zorro and bush dog, living in humid forests, have less need for 'radiators' than does the fennec of the deserts.

Small male dominant

The male zorro at Brookfield Zoo was always surrounded by a musky aroma from its anal glands, but there was hardly any noticeable aroma from the female. The male was one third smaller than the female with a smaller head and more slender muzzle but he did dominate her, taking precedence at feeding times and not allowing her to feed until he was replete.

Obscure relations

Apart from its superficial resemblance to the bush dog, the short-eared zorro seems to be unrelated to any of the fox- or wolf-like dogs. With its short ears, the pattern of the coat, the proportions of the skull and its cat-like gait, it appears to be unique. This makes it noteworthy and the absence of any observations on its behaviour make speculation worthwhile, as in the false killer whale (p 1225) whose habits have largely been pieced together from observations of stranded animals. Even the relationships of well-known dogs have presented difficulties because, apart from size, there is very little variation in their skeletons, all of them being unspecialised, long-distance runners. The relationships of the dog family have now been investigated by comparisons of their social behaviour and the true position of the zorro will probably not be known until more zorros can be found and studied. So we end this encyclopedia, if not with a mystery animal then with one about which further study may reveal many interesting features.

class	**Mammalia**
order	**Carnivora**
family	**Canidae**
genus & species	***Atelocynus microtis***

Special Contents

A closer look at some of the basic aspects of the Animal Kingdom.

The scientific classification of animals

In order to classify animals by their relationships and to make international understanding easier zoologists have evolved a far-reaching system of Greek or Latin based names for animals and groupings of animals. This scheme not only gives every different kind of animal its own internationally known name but also fixes its position in relation to the rest of the Animal Kingdom.

The principal categories are as follows. The Animal Kingdom is itself, of course, the largest of them, comprising all animals. The Kingdom is divided first into *phyla*. Although the majority of the commonly known animals fall into one phylum, the Chordata (which includes the vertebrates or back-boned animals), there are very many phyla at the more primitive and widely divergent end of the scale.

The phylum is divided into *classes*: one such is the class Mammalia, containing all the mammals. Classes are again divided into *orders*, distinguishing, for example, the Carnivora from the Primates. After orders come *families*: the apes, for instance, form a family within the order of Primates.

This illustration traces the lion Panthera leo *through its classification, with other examples of genus, family, order, class and phylum.*

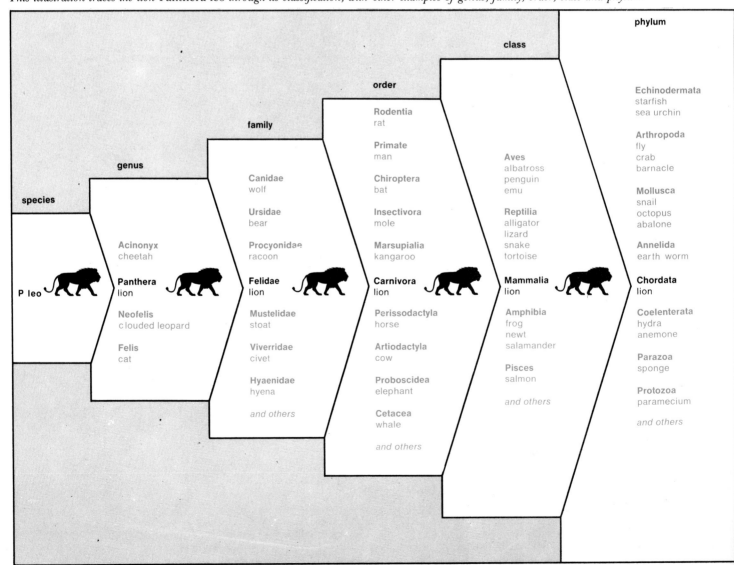

The subdivision of the family is the *genus*, containing very closely related animals; and finally comes the *species*, which defines an animal exactly. The normal scientific way of referring to an animal is by its generic and specific names together. Thus the lion is *Panthera leo: Panthera* is the genus (which also contains the closely related tiger, leopard and jaguar), and *leo*, the specific name (and Latin for lion), narrows the field to the lion alone.

To sum up, let us follow the lion up through the scheme of classification. The genus and species are *Panthera leo*; it belongs to the family Felidae, with all the cat-like animals; the Felidae are part of the order Carnivora, with the other flesh-eating mammals; these join all other mammals in the class Mammalia, which in turn belongs with the birds, fishes and others to the phylum Chordata; and the Chordata belong with all other animals to the Animal Kingdom, as opposed to the plants.

Other subdivisions

Increasing scientific knowledge has made necessary the creation of additional groupings falling between the existing ones. Thus there are subkingdoms, subphyla, subclasses, infraclasses, superorders, suborders, superfamilies, subfamilies, tribes (division of subfamilies), and finally subspecies, or races, which describe local variants of what is basically one species.

Recognition

Species' names can always be recognised because they consist of two words (generic and specific names) printed in italic type — for example *Ursus arctos* (brown bear). For closer identification the sub-specific name may be added, giving for example *Ursus arctos syriacus* (Syrian bear) as distinct from *Ursus arctos arctos* (European brown bear). In cases of repetition the generic name may be designated by its initial, so *U. arctos*.

Other group names are printed in roman type but with capital letters. Family names are recognisable because they always end in -idae: thus Felidae, the cat family, or Canidae, the dog family. Similarly, superfamilies end in -oidea, subfamilies in -inae and tribes in -ini.

For most groups there is no rule for the ending of order names; however, orders of birds always end in -iformes: thus Sphenisciformes, the penguins. Larger groupings than orders offer no means of quick recognition, except that phyla and classes always end in -a — but so may orders and others.

Warning

It must be remembered that names are only names; there is no universal truth about them. Thus classification is always subject to alteration in the light of new scientific discoveries; also, zoologists can disagree about a particular question and divide into two or more camps, each using different terminology. In addition, the same animal may be discovered in different parts of the world and so acquire different names, which take time to sort out.

It must be remembered also that the animal world is in a constant state of change; animals invade new environments and adapt to them, or exploit new food sources, eventually changing enough to be called new species.

An acceptable definition of a species was put forward by the ornithologist Mayr in 1940: 'species are groups of actually or potentially interbreeding populations which are reproductively isolated from other such groups'. Among the 8 500 species of birds, however, there are several scores of species on the point of dividing into new ones (see *Bird Speciation* p 2707). Agreement is far from being reached about these alone; the whole Animal Kingdom contains nearly a million species!

For these reasons reference books are not unanimous in their naming of animals in every case: this does not mean that one of them is wrong, but that for some reason the nomenclature is undecided.

King of beasts — a majestic lion Panthera leo *relaxes at the end of the day, catching the last rays of sunlight.*

Robert Grant

Brand names in animal life

Before a manufacturer can market a new product he must give it a brand name, otherwise prospective customers will not know how to ask for it. To avoid confusion the name must be different from any other. A hundred years ago the problem of naming saleable goods was nothing like as acute as it is today, because the number of items was relatively small.

We have an exact parallel with the naming of animals. In the time of the Ancient Greeks little attempt was made to distinguish between animals of the same kind. The word 'eagle', for example, did duty for almost any large bird of prey that flew by day. With the accumulation of knowledge, and with scholars of different nationalities and languages studying animals, there arose a need to say which kind of eagle you were writing about and in a language which everybody could understand. The language problem was solved by using Latin to describe animals, but this was still based on the common names current in various languages. Even with the relatively few animals named by the beginning of the 17th century, at the time when the Royal Society was still to be founded, confusion was already beginning to creep in, and with the naming of more and more animals, the confusion was increasing.

It fell to a Swedish botanist, Carl von Linné (better known by the Latinised form of his name Linnaeus) to come to the rescue with his Binomial System published in his book *Systema Naturae* in 1757. This work went into several different editions, each an improvement of the last, and it is the 10th edition published in 1758 which is now accepted as the standard.

In the *Systema Naturae* a cat is given the Latin name *Felis catus*. 'Cat' may be similar in different languages but there is at least enough difference to make it at times unrecognisable. In French, for example, it is *chat*. In German, however, it is *die Katze*. So we could go on for the rest of the languages. But *Felis catus* is recognisable to all.

The layman may ask why we do not use the ordinary common names. As we see again and again in this Encyclopedia one animal will not only have a different common name in different countries but also in different parts of the English-speaking world. Conversely, one common name may be used for half-a-dozen different kinds of animals in different parts of the world. With one agreed scientific name all this can be avoided, but that name must be in a dead language, otherwise scientists of various countries would never have agreed which language should be used, whether it should be English, French or German.

Often the scientific names are derived from Ancient Greek instead of Latin, but the same principle applies, a dead language is being used. Linnaeus by a stroke of genius presented the scientific world with a master tool at a time when the number of known animals had reached the 'staggering' total of 50 000. He did this just in time to create order out of a growing chaos. We have only to compare this 50 000 with the total of known animals today to appreciate what we owe to Linnaeus. New species are being created at the rate of around 10 000 every year. Estimates of the total of known (that is described) species vary from one million upwards or over 20 times the number known in the days of Linnaeus.

There is another objection often voiced by the layman, and especially by the naturalist, that so often the scientific names are

different from one book to another. The explanation is to be found in the history of trying to make the Linnaean system work.

As the list of published names of animal species mounted a further confusion began to creep in. For example, the harvest mouse of Europe had escaped scientific observation, surprisingly, until the 18th century. Then in 1767 Gilbert White found it in Hampshire but he did not publish his observation until 1789, in his *Natural History of Selborne*. He did mention it, however, to Thomas Pennant, who, in his *British Zoology* (1768) referred to it as the less long-tailed fieldmouse. White gave it the name of *Mus minimus* but in the meantime Pallas, a German-born Russian naturalist had also found it and had published a description of it in 1771 as *Mus minutus*. During the next 50 to 60 years this mouse was found in other parts of Europe and given different names by different authors.

This is a good example of what has been happening with very many animals. Eventually an International Commission was set up and it was accepted that in future the law of priority should rule. That is, the scientific name of an animal should be the earliest one given to it. In the case of the harvest mouse this would be *minutus*. Not uncommonly, however, a scientific name would have been widely used perhaps for a century, and printed in a number of books. Then an earlier name would be found, and the law of priority would have to be enforced. But not everybody would become aware of this immediately, and so authors would continue turning out their books, some using one name and some using another for the same animal.

All this is unfortunate, and the possibility of its happening again is still with us. We are reaching something like stability

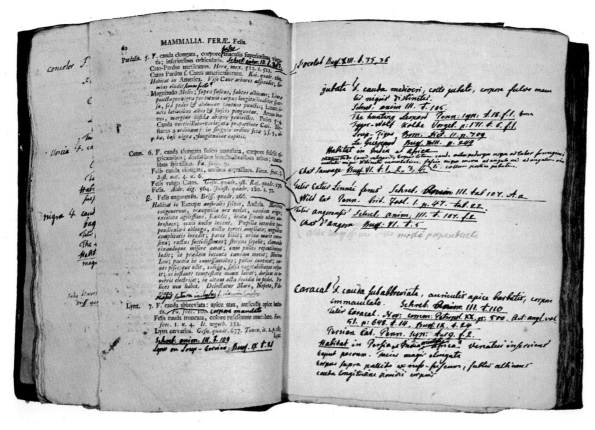

An early edition of Linnaeus' Systema Naturae, *the first published attempt to classify the Animal Kingdom by logical reference to the form of the animals. It was the basis of the binomial system of naming animals. The illustration shows a spread of the book devoted to the cat family. His criteria for the genus* **Felis** *were a rough tongue and retractable claws. He placed this under the 'savage' beasts — those with six sharp primary teeth and single canines (he referred to only one side of one jaw at a time).*
The handwritten notes on the facing page are additions and corrections by the author's son.

but it has not yet been achieved. Therefore, in presenting the scientific names of animals in this Encyclopedia we must achieve a temporary stability by following certain authorities. For mammals, we have followed *Mammals of the World* by Ernest P Walker (1964); for the birds, *The New Dictionary of Birds* by Landsborough Thomson (1964).

For the rest we have used the following:
Living Reptiles of the World by Carl P Schmidt and Robert P Inger
Living Amphibians of the World by Doris M Cochran
Living Fishes of the World by Earl S Herald, but with modifications based on a monograph by P H Greenwood and others in the

Bulletin of the American Museum of Natural History volume 131 part 4, 1966.

For the invertebrates we have used mainly *Living Insects of the World*, by Alexander B and Elsie Klots, *Living Invertebrates of the World* by Ralph Buchsbaum and Lorus J Milne, and *A Classification of Living Animals* by Rothschild, 1961.

Harvest mice Mus minutus. *First discovered in 1769 by Gilbert White in Hampshire, England, the same species was found independently by other authors all over Europe in the next 50 to 60 years, and given widely different names. The priority rule gave it its present name.*

The division between the Plant and the Animal Kingdoms

At the everyday level, there is seldom any doubt as to whether a plant is a plant or an animal is an animal. Animals move about, eat complex foods, and are not coloured green by photosynthetic pigments; plants do not wander in search of complex foods, but manufacture the more elaborate substances they need from carbon dioxide and the many simple, inorganic nutrients and water which they obtain from the soil.

Among the simple single-celled organisms which most people seldom see or notice, it becomes more difficult to apply any strict definitions. In the microscopic world of the single-celled organism, the term 'animal' or 'plant' must be modified before it can be made to fit into one of the two groupings.

The microscopic organisms included in the phylum Protista are many and varied. As they are single-celled, each cell has to perform all the functions necessary for life. In multicellular forms these functions are carried out by different tissues and organs. The single cell must be able to feed, grow and reproduce while totally exposed to a hostile environment, without the benefits of very complex multicellular protective structures. Hence the seemingly simple single-celled organism is really very complex.

Because the Protista form such a large group, and each cell has to be self-contained, it is small wonder that some of the cells have characters which by the standards of other groups would place them in both the plant and the animal kingdoms. Because of these facts, scientists consider it likely that both plants and animals may have evolved from primitive ancestors of this group.

Protista fall naturally into four groups: three of them are colourless and have animal characteristics, the fourth group contains both coloured and colourless forms.

Chlorophyll coloured

The coloured ones are often green due to chlorophyll in the cells. The colourless amoeboid forms are clearly animal and feed by engulfing and digesting food particles. The organisms in this group do not have a regular shape and move by flowing movements of the cytoplasm.

The ciliated organisms have a regular shape. They can also move, by the action of cilia: short whip-like organelles arranged in groups over all or part of the cell surface. Ciliates also feed by engulfing animal and plant matter and digesting it within the cell. Like the amoebae, ciliates can clearly be considered animal.

The class Sporozoa are mainly parasites. An example is *Plasmodium,* which causes malaria in man. At one stage this minute organism lives in the red blood corpuscles, obtaining its food in relatively complex forms directly from its animal host.

Whips for movement

The class Mastigophora may be coloured or colourless. They move with one or two whip-like flagella, longer forms of cilia. The flagellum is itself very complex. It is remarkable as wherever it is found in the plant

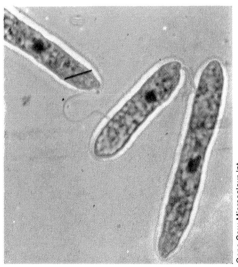

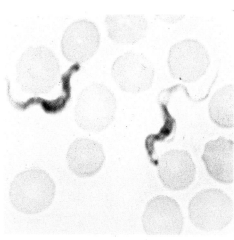

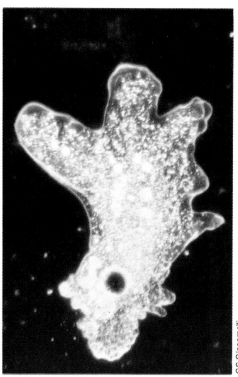

Top: **Euglena** *is a protistan with both plant and animal features, since it contains chlorophyll and can also move about.*
Centre: A Mastigophoran with animal characteristics, **Trypanosoma gambiense** *is the blood parasite which causes sleeping sickness.*
Bottom: **Chaos diffluens** *— the amoeba of school zoology classes — is colourless and moves by flowing of the cytoplasm in 'pseudopodia'.*

or animal world, it has a uniform structure. For practical purposes, within the flagellates the dividing line between the plant and animal kingdoms is taken to be the possession or not of photosynthetic pigments, but this often separates closely related forms. Consequently both botanists and zoologists have devised different systems of classification for both types of organism.

The organism *Euglena,* a flagellate protistan, exhibits characters which are by no means typical of the group as a whole and illustrates how in the single-celled forms the idea of plants or animals as completely separate life-forms has to be modified.

Euglena gracilis is coloured due to the possession of plastids (specialised plant structures) which contain the photosynthetic pigments chlorophyll a and b. *Euglena* swims in a complex way by means of a single external flagellum. Although all forms of the family Euglenophyceae (the botanical class to which *Euglena* belongs) basically have two flagella, *Euglena,* in common with many members of the class, has one of the two greatly reduced to an internal remnant and uses only one for swimming.

The chlorophylls which this organism possesses are characteristic of the 'higher' plants, and of the green algae. The algae are a mixed plant group which includes organisms ranging from single cells to very large seaweeds. The food reserve, paramylon, which *Euglena* stores, is chemically more closely related to that found in the red algae, brown algae, and the diatoms than to the starch reserves of the green plants. So while *Euglena* and its relatives have features which make these organisms unusual, they do have several features characteristic of the major plant groups, as well as something in common with other groups of protistans.

Controlled experiments

Other strains of *Euglena,* when kept in the dark, become bleached, lose their pigmentation, and being deprived of light, cannot photosynthesise. But if 'fed' with some simple organic compounds, these strains can live for long periods in the dark. In this way these organisms are showing one of the principal 'animal' features of feeding on complex substances, rather than the plant feature of making their own food by photosynthesis. Other strains such as *Astasia longa* are found naturally in a bleached condition, but are otherwise typical forms of *Euglena,* and are obviously very similar to *E. gracilis. Euglenopsis edax* actually ingests solid food particles but is otherwise a typical euglenoid form.

Thus organisms like *Euglena* show within their group a range of animal as well as plant features. Similar ranges are shown to a lesser degree in other groups of flagellate algal cells, some forms requiring the presence of vitamin B12 before they can grow. A requirement for vitamins is certainly not a plant feature but one which is typical of animals.

The example of *Euglena* does show that at the very 'low' levels of organisation the boundary between animals and plants often becomes blurred, and this picture becomes more and more confused as more detail is considered.

Plants

Usually green due to the presence of the photosynthetic pigment chlorophyll. This enables them to trap the energy of sunlight for the manufacture of complex food substances from simple raw materials in the soil (water and mineral salts) and the air (carbon dioxide).

Usually remain in one place as unable to move about—eg rooted in the soil. Reproduction involves passive means such as pollination.

The cells usually have a thick cellulose wall so that their shape is rigid, and the cytoplasm often contains large vacuoles.

Animals

Do not contain chlorophyll and are unable to build up their own complex food substances. Instead they must find foodstuffs in which these have already been manufactured by plants. Digestion within the body breaks these down in order to release energy.

Usually able to move about freely to look for food, and also to search actively for a mate.

The cells are not surrounded by a thick wall and do not usually contain large vacuoles.

Ultrastructure of animal cells

Most living matter is built on a cellular plan. Cells vary in size from approximately 10–100 microns* and may be divided into a central nuclear region, surrounded by cytoplasm which is enclosed by a cell membrane. The nucleus, which determines the activity and general properties of the cell, contains the genetical apparatus, while the cytoplasm includes the organelles involved in the processes of energy release and synthesis of macromolecules.

Limited resolution

The ultrastructure of cells remained a complete mystery until the development of the electron microscope in the 20th century permitted the finely detailed structure of different types of cells to be compared. In this instrument a beam of accelerated, short wavelength electrons is used to produce resolutions of 2–10 Ångstroms.**

Unfortunately, electrons do not penetrate very far in air, and thus the microscope is constructed around a vacuum system. Since the electrons have to pass through the cells to produce an image, very thin (approx. 500 Ångstrom) sections have to be cut by means of special microtomes. The tissues are fixed, dehydrated and then embedded in plastic and the thin sections, supported on fine grids, are viewed in the microscope, which can magnify up to 250 000 times. Since as many as 200 thin sections may be cut from a 10-micron wide cell, the three-dimensional image of the cell's ultrastructure has to be built up with reference to many sections.

The nucleus

The nucleus is the most obvious component of the cells and is clearly seen in low-power photomicrographs. Nuclei vary in size and shape in different tissues; they may be round, elliptical, indented or even branching. The chromosomes are not visible in most cells of adult animals. They are only seen in actively dividing cells where they are formed from an aggregation of the compound DNA (deoxyribonucleic acid).

In each nucleus there are one or more nucleoli which have a high concentration of RNA (ribonucleic acid) and these are usually seen as dense granular masses.

The nucleus is separated from the cytoplasm by a double membrane system, which contains pores which communicate with the cell's other membrane systems.

Unit membranes

The so-called unit membranes, found throughout the cell, consist of two layers of fat molecules enclosed by a layer of protein molecules on either side. The thickness of the membrane varies from approximately 60–100Å. The plasma membrane surrounding the cell acts not only as the structural barrier between the cytoplasm and the exterior, but also, by its permeability, controls the passage of materials such as food and waste products into and out of the cell.

'Powerhouse' of the cell

The most distinctive organelles in the cytoplasm are the mitochondria, the number

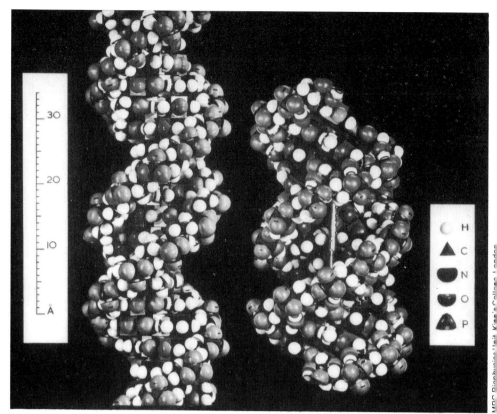

Molecular models of deoxyribonucleic acid DNA (left) and ribonucleic acid RNA (right). DNA is the hereditary material of the chromosomes; the molecule is a double helix with cross bridges, and the arrangement of the atoms in the latter is the basis of the so-called genetic code. RNA is similar to DNA in both structure and function, and occurs in several forms in the cell. The atoms making up the molecule are: H=hydrogen, C=carbon, N=nitrogen, O=oxygen and P=phosphorus. The scale on the left is in Ångstrom units.

present being related to the metabolic activity of the cell; the higher the metabolic rate, the more mitochondria are present. Each tissue has mitochondria of characteristic shapes and sizes, but all have double membranes, the inner one being folded inwards to form cristae. The mitochondria are called the 'powerhouses' of the cells since they are involved in the release of energy from carbohydrates and fats. The energy is taken up in the phosphate bonds of the ATP molecule (adenosine triphosphate). The enzymes involved in this conversion are arranged in a definite sequence on the membranes of the mitochondria. ATP molecules can move to all parts of the cell to release this energy, needed for all the metabolic processes.

Cytoskeleton

The cytoplasm contains an intricate cytoskeleton of membranes. This three-dimensional network of membrane-lined canals, which connect to the nucleus and possibly to the exterior, is called the endoplasmic reticulum. It may be rough- or smooth-surfaced, depending on whether it has granules embedded in its walls. These small dense particles composed of RNA are called ribosomes. They are involved in the manufacture of proteins, which pass into the canals of the endoplasmic reticulum and some are eventually exported from the cell. Other ribosomes, not associated with membranes, produce fibrous proteins in the cytoplasm. The smooth-walled canals connect with the rough ones and in some cells are also involved in the synthesis of lipids (fats) and hormones.

Golgi's discovery

Some areas of the smooth endoplasmic reticulum are arranged in an intricate and characteristic form called the Golgi complex. This consists of flattened sacs arranged in a cup or crescentic form, with associated small vesicles, vacuoles and granules. The Golgi complex is involved in forming membranes and packaging proteins from the rough endoplasmic reticulum into granules for discharge to another cell.

The cell's digestive system

Another class of organelles present in the cytoplasm may also be derived from the Golgi complex; these are the lysosomes which were first identified by Christian de Duve in 1955. They vary greatly in size and content, but are basically granules with a single membrane containing a variety of acid hydrolytic enzymes.

Lysosomes function as part of the cell's digestive system, as they may fuse with vacuoles containing engulfed foodstuffs taken in by the cell. In other circumstances such as when a cell is injured, parts of the cytoplasm may be engulfed into lysosomes and be digested. This 'self-digestion' often repairs the damage, but in extreme cases of damage, active hydrolases are released into the cytoplasm to remove the dying cells from the tissues.

Ultrastructural research has gone a long way to elucidating the details of the structure and possible functions of the cell and its organelles.

* There are 1 000 microns (μ) in a millimetre (mm).
** There are 10 000 Ångstroms (Å) in a micron (μ).

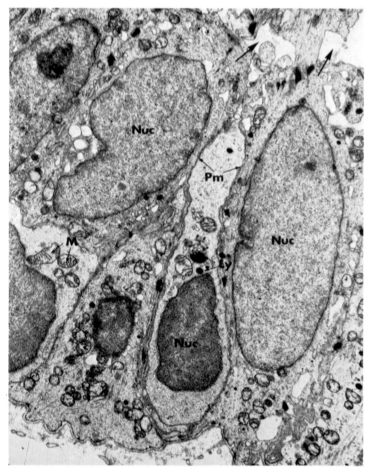

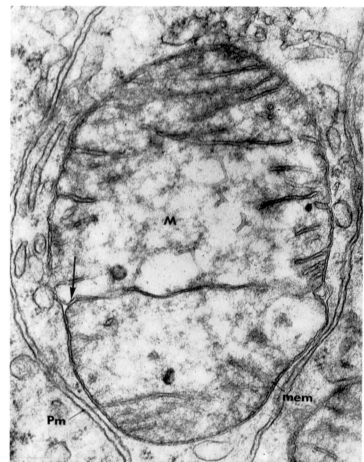

△ *Electron micrograph of stained epithelial cells, showing nuclei (Nuc), mitochondria (M), lysosomes (Ly) and plasma membrane surrounding each cell (Pm). Spaces between the cells are arrowed.* (×13 000).

▽ *Nucleus with nuclear membrane (Nm) broached by a pore (arrowed). In the surrounding cytoplasm are the Golgi complex (GC), and endoplasmic reticulum (Er) with ribosomes (R).* (×60 000).

△ *Close-up of a mitochondrion in the cell cytoplasm. The double membrane construction (mem) is clearly shown, with the inner membrane folded inwards into cristae (arrowed).* (×75 000).

▽ *Part of the cytoplasm of a cell with a prominent Golgi complex and associated vesicles (Ves). The flattened sacs of smooth endoplasmic reticulum arranged in a cup shape are arrowed.* (×60 000).

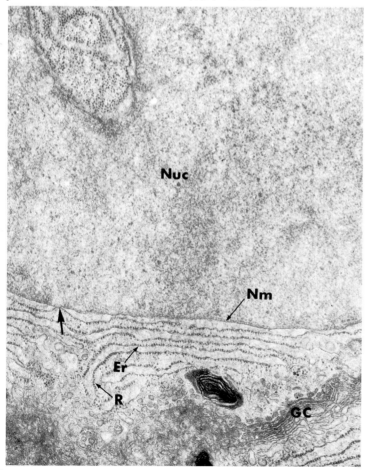

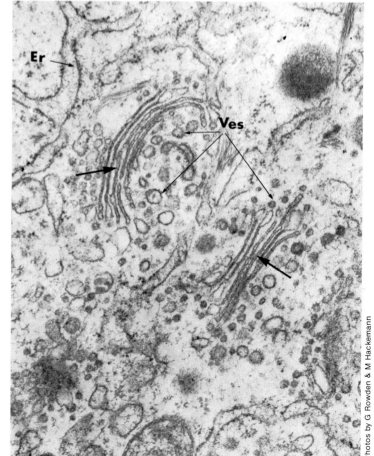

Photos by G Rowden & M Hackemann

Cell division:
Mitosis and Meiosis

A concept central to modern biology is that all animals and plants are made up of living microscopic units called cells, and that these only arise from pre-existing cells. A cell has two main regions, the cytoplasm, which is jelly-like, and the nucleus which contains most of the hereditary information of the cell and which serves to direct the many chemical reactions taking place in the cytoplasm necessary for life. All animals begin life as a single cell, called a zygote, which is formed by the fusion of two specialised cells, a sperm from the father and an egg from the mother. Since the adult animal contains many millions of cells this implies some mechanism whereby the single zygote cell gives rise to all the cells of the adult body. Research has shown that normally one cell divides to form two cells, the two then divide to give four cells which produce eight, then sixteen and so on, until the recognisable form of the animal as we know it becomes apparent. This kind of cell division is called mitosis, and results in the production of a large number of cells which all have the same kind of hereditary material in their nuclei.

Microscopic examination of the nuclei of many kinds of cells has shown that when a cell is ready to divide, very thin thread-like objects become visible; these structures are called chromosomes. Each animal has a typical number of chromosomes in the cells of its body; thus the body cells of the hamster have 22 chromosomes, those of man have 46, and those of the crayfish have about 200. This number is called the diploid number of chromosomes; half of these are obtained from the mother and half from the father during sexual reproduction. The sperm and egg cells which unite to form the first cell of a new individual, each have only half the number of chromosomes found in a typical body cell. If this were not so the number of chromosomes in the body cells of animals would be doubled every time a new individual was formed. Thus at one of the cell divisions which produce the sperm and egg a reduction in the number of chromosomes to one half that of normal body cells occurs—this special reduction division is called meiosis, and the half number of chromosomes is called the haploid number. In addition to the halving of the number of chromosomes important rearrangements of the hereditary material also occur in meiosis. The sequence, mechanics, and chemistry of these changes become very important in the understanding of the inheritance of all those characteristics which make up the appearance and behaviour of the individual animal.

Mitosis

The first part of mitosis is called prophase and during this the chromosomes become visible as thin thread-like objects which are doubled throughout their length. Each half chromosome is called a chromatid and they are held together at only one point by a structure called the centromere, although they may be closely wrapped around each other. During prophase the chromosomes contract in length and this results in them becoming thicker. At the end of prophase the chromosomes lie freely in the cytoplasm of the cell since the membrane around the nucleus breaks down.

The appearance of a structure called the spindle marks the beginning of metaphase. The spindle stretches from one pole of the cell to the other and soon after its formation the centromeres of the chromosomes become attached to it at the very centre, the equator of the cell. The centromeres then divide, marking the beginning of anaphase, and appear to repel each other, pulling their attached chromatids to opposite poles of the cell. Thus the original chromosomes are divided into two. At the poles of the cell

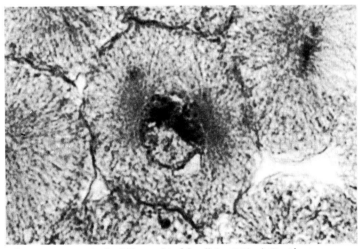

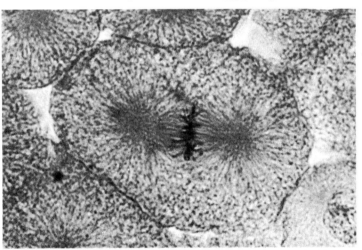

The four stages of mitosis in a whitefish cell (×650). △ *Prophase: the chromosomes are visible as a darkly-staining area and the nuclear membrane is beginning to break down.*

△ *Metaphase: free in the cytoplasm, the chromosomes are attached by their centromeres to the equatorial region of the spindle, a special structure which appears only during cell division.*

▽ *Anaphase: the centromeres divide in two, and draw their attached chromatids to opposite poles of the spindle. The chromatids become the new chromosomes, which have thus reproduced themselves.*

▽ *Telophase: the chromosomes gradually become invisible by known staining techniques, a nuclear membrane develops around each group of chromosomes, and the cytoplasm divides to form two new cells.*

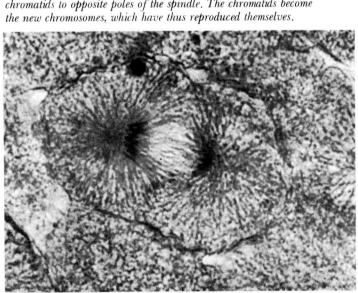

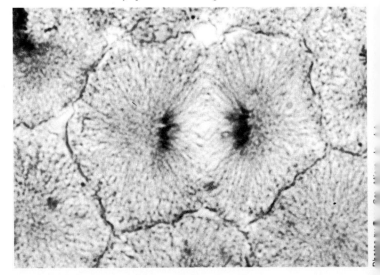

the two groups of chromosomes, the former chromatids, undergo changes which result in their eventual disappearance from view; this stage is known as telophase. Finally the cytoplasm of the cell divides into two halves and two new cells are produced each with the same number of chromosomes, the same number as found in the parent cell.

Meiosis

The type of cell division known as meiosis consists of two divisions of the cell with only one division of the chromosomes. Chromosomes are built up of a substance called deoxyribonucleic acid – DNA – and protein. DNA carries within its structure, in units called genes, most of the hereditary information necessary for the development of the individual. The importance of meiosis lies in the way in which genes are exchanged between chromosomes thus creating new combinations of hereditary material during cell division. Meiosis in adult animals is confined to special organs of the body; in the male these are the testes and in the female the ovaries, producing sperm and eggs respectively. Although there are a number of different stages in the production of sperm and eggs only the meiotic division will be described here.

In a cell about to undergo meiosis the chromosomes become visible as single, thin, thread-like structures, often with a beaded appearance. The chromosomes soon begin to pair up two by two, one of the pair being derived from the father of the individual and the other from the mother. The pairs of chromosomes are called homologous chromosomes and they match each other perfectly, gene for gene. The chromosomes of each pair become so closely coiled around each other that they appear as one; the term bivalent is applied to the pair in this condition. Shortly after this the two chromosomes forming the bivalent begin to pull apart and it becomes evident that each chromosome consists of two chromatids making a total of four in each bivalent. The chromosomes of each bivalent are joined at certain points along their length, each point is called a chiasma. The latter represent points of interchange between a chromatid of one chromosome and a chromatid of the other chromosome of the bivalent; chiasmata do not form between chromatids of the same chromosome. Genes are thus exchanged between the chromosomes. Eventually the chiasmata begin to disappear and the bivalents move to the cell centre.

Formation of the spindle as in mitosis marks the beginning of metaphase I. The bivalents become arranged on the spindle at the equator of the cell and anaphase I begins when the chromosomes of each bivalent lose contact with each other and begin to move to opposite poles of the cell, pulled by their centromeres which do not divide. At each pole at telophase I is a group of chromosomes which number only one half that found in the parent cell.

Each of the two telophase cells formed usually immediately enters a second division which is very similar to mitosis. The chromosomes arrange themselves at the equator of the cell in metaphase II, the centromeres divide and the chromatids move to the poles of the cell during anaphase II. Telophase II follows and gradually the chromosomes disappear from view and the cytoplasm becomes divided up between the new cells produced.

Meiosis thus results in the production of four cells, each cell having the halved or haploid number of chromosomes. When haploid sperm and egg unite during fertilisation in a sexually reproducing animal species, the diploid number of chromosomes as found in the ordinary body cells of the animal is restored. This demonstrates the significance of meiosis in that it allows new unions of hereditary material to occur, so that the animal species can best adapt to a constantly changing environment.

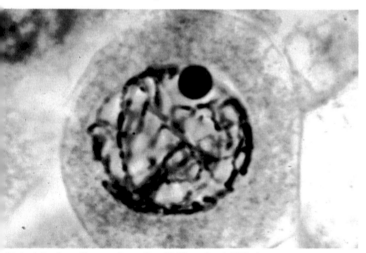

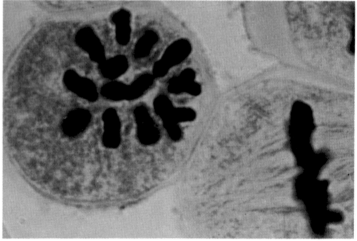

Meiosis in the pollen mother cells of **Lilium** *(× 1 920) demonstrates principles common to plants and animals.* △ *Leptotene: one of several preliminary stages, showing thread-like chromosomes and a nucleolus.*

▽ *Anaphase I: the centromeres do not divide, but the chromosomes of each bivalent part company and are dragged to opposite poles of the cell. This accomplishes the halving of chromosome numbers.*

△ *Metaphase I: the bivalents or pairs of homologous chromosomes are attached by their centromeres to the spindle equator. The cell on the left has been sectioned through the plane of the equator.*

▽ *Telophase I: the chromosomes cluster together but though the cytoplasm is dividing in two no nuclear membrane appears, because a mitotic division will follow immediately, to give four new cells.*

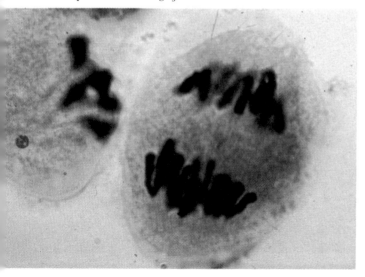

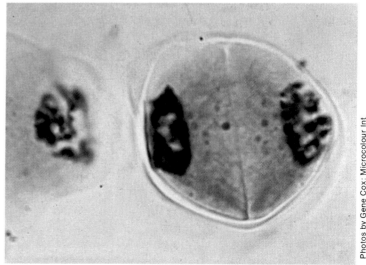

Photos by Gene Cox: Microcolour Int

Charles Darwin 1809-1882

The 'Theory of Evolution' is usually coupled with Darwin, whose genius in the late 1850's gave the world the new idea of natural selection.

Darwin was born in Shrewsbury in 1809, the son of a wealthy doctor. At the local public school he received the usual course of Latin and Greek verses with classical geography and history. It is interesting to note that this curriculum did not contain any natural history and so Darwin, to satisfy his great interest in this field, read books on natural history and foreign travel, performed chemical experiments in the garden shed, and wandered about the countryside fishing, shooting and collecting minerals, rocks and insects. This, of course, made his headmaster openly criticise him, and his father thought his pursuits were disgraceful.

This supposedly idle boy was therefore sent to Edinburgh to study medicine. The sight of two operations performed under the conditions of that time — local anaesthetics had not been brought into use — revolted the 17-year-old Darwin. After two years, when it was quite apparent that he was totally unsuited for medical life, he returned to Shrewsbury. His family now decided that he should study for the Church. Charles did not seem to object violently, so 1828 found him in Cambridge. His social life, however, seemed to take him away from religious study. He mixed with young men of whom his father certainly disapproved and he enjoyed wine, song and cards to the full. The outcome of these days was that insufficient study rewarded him with merely a BA pass degree.

On graduating in 1821, Darwin was all prepared to take Holy Orders when fate intervened to set an apparently unambitious man with little distinction on the way to show the world his spark of genius and depth of reasoning.

On the advice of his professor and friend, John Henslow, Darwin joined HMS *Beagle* on a voyage to South America as an unpaid naturalist.

Up to his departure from England Darwin had no cause to doubt the immutability of species. He had studied Sir Charles Lyell's *Principles of Geology* and acquired a general background of 'uniformitarianism' rather

Unpaid naturalist to a mapping voyage, Charles Darwin formulated ideas that changed zoology.

than 'catastrophism'. Certain observations, however, set off Darwin's revolt against the immutability of species. On his trip to the Galapagos Islands he was amazed by the differences among finches (see p 615). He asked himself why such a fantastic number of species had been created in the islands. He also compared the fauna of the Galapagos with that of the Cape Verde Islands where, in spite of similar physical conditions, the animal species were totally different; those of the Galapagos resembled those of South America while Cape Verde Islands' fauna resembled that of Africa.

In his South American mainland travels, Darwin noticed that animals, although different species, showed a great deal of resemblance to one another, and they were found in regions separated only by a slight distance.

The fossil evidence of the Pampas region also amazed Darwin, as large fossil mammals showed armour similar to that of the armadillos living in that area.

These observations, with many others, gradually caused Darwin to form new views on how animal and plant species had come to be. On his return Darwin was convinced

of evolution, but how these changes had taken place still eluded him. He had various ideas and wrote numerous notes, but he kept them secret, except to his closest friends, Lyell and Hooker. His secret beliefs were that the species had evolved by natural processes from a few simple primordial forms or possibly even one form.

Darwin led a secluded life at Downe, in Kent, with his wife, a daughter of the Wedgewood family. He took great interest in the breeding methods of domestic animals and 'fancy types' such as pigeons. He realised that breeders always chose certain characteristics and continued to select required variants through several generations, until the desired new 'breed' was obtained. These bred true only if mated between themselves. This 'artificial selection' gave a first clue, but he still wondered how this selection could operate in the wild without any conscious direction.

When Darwin read the essay *'The principles of population'* by Thomas Robert Malthus, an English clergyman, he realised that under the intense conditions of animals and plants competing to live, any variations which continued would have to be those

which increased the organism's ability to leave fertile offspring. Those variations which decreased the animals' or plants' numbers would eventually be eliminated and thus 'natural selection' took place.

Although Darwin had formulated the framework of his evolutionary theory in 1838 it was another 20 years before the public were to learn of his revolutionary ideas, when his hand was forced by Alfred Russel Wallace who held the same views on an evolutionary theory.

Darwin, on the advice of friends, had his own thoughts of evolution and those of Wallace, read as a joint communication to the Linnaean Society in July 1858. The following year Darwin's *'Origin of species by means of natural selection, or the preservation of favoured races in the struggle of life'* was published. Although the religious Victorians were eager to read it, they were shocked and disgusted by the implications of the idea that life had changed during time and was not created as told in the Bible.

A bitter struggle then arose between pro- and anti-evolutionists. Darwin just let them fight and still led a secluded life until his death in 1882.

J-B de Lamarck 1744—1829
A colleague of Cuvier who suggested that a transformation of species might occur by the 'inheritance of acquired characters'.

C Linnaeus 1707—1829
Naturalist who introduced a system of classifying plants and animals. The Linnaeus system in outline is still used today.

AR Wallace 1823—1913
Reached same conclusion as Darwin. Argued species evolved slowly and that survival of the fittest would lead to new types.

G Cuvier 1769—1832
Rejected all ideas of changes in animal form and stated that life had been repeatedly wiped out and replaced by new species.

G Mendel 1822—1884
Solved the mechanism of inheritance and discovered the conformity of the transmission of characters from parents to offspring.

Voyage of the *Beagle*

Galapagos Islands
How each island had its own peculiar and distinctive types of plants, tortoises and finches fitting into a certain niche in the environment. Not special creation but transformed from ies on South American mainland, which basically resemble them.

Cape Verde Islands
Noticed species entirely different to Galapagos species although in similar locations and conditions.
Birds here share a common ancestor with the birds of Africa.

South American mainland
Saw the hares of South America are built on the South American rodent plan as all these rodents are descended from a common ancestor.
Fossil **Glyptodon** found. Resembles living armadillos as both had a common ancestor.

Falmouth L 2 Oct 1836 · Plymouth
S 27 Dec 1831

Azores
L 20 Sept 1836

Cape Verde Island   L 16 Jan 1832 L 31 Aug 1836

Galapagos Islands L 16 Sept 1835   S 20 Oct 1835

Bahia.

St. Helena

Mauritius

New Zealand
L 21 Dec 1835

Rio de Janeiro
L 5 Apr 1832

Cape
Town

Hobart
L 5 Feb 1836

anded
sailed

Falkland Islands
Shipped a great sea 13 Jan 1833

A detailed map studying the voyage of HMS **Beagle,** *which lasted between the years 1831-1836.*

Evolution of Man

Evolution binds the living world together, and there is no doubt about it—evolution is a fact. Although it is still conveniently known as 'The Theory of Evolution', it has passed the stage of being a working hypothesis, and to all intents and purposes has been adequately confirmed as a fact.

The most direct way to appreciate the reality of evolution is to see it in action; and this has happened. Considering the long span of life itself (the earliest organism's remains have been found in rocks dated at 3 000 million years ago!) one cannot expect to see much change occurring within a single human lifetime. Nonetheless, quite a number of new races, or subspecies, of animals have arisen in the past 100 years; and several new *species* of plants. At Kew Gardens, surprised botanists discovered a new species of primrose *Primula kewensis* which developed from an accidental cross between two other species. In this case, we can observe evolution by direct mutation, in a process known as allopolyploidy. Although there are indications that this occurs in wild plants too, it is not the usual mode of speciation, and in animals (at least those which reproduce sexually) new forms result from natural selection.

Natural selection is nothing complicated or frightening. People are usually surprised to find how straightforward and logical it is. If a mutation—a spontaneous change in the hereditary material, occurring in just one or a few individuals of the population—is disadvantageous, then by natural selection, 'survival of the fittest', the individuals bearing it will not survive for long. If, on the other hand, the mutation puts its bearers at an advantage, then by natural selection its bearers will survive in proportionally higher numbers than those without it, until it spreads and takes over the whole population. It is as simple as that. There is nothing mysterious or metaphysical about it, no 'urge to evolve' or anything like that. If a creature is adequately adapted to its environment, and the environment does not change, then it will not evolve because no mutation can be advantageous to it: the coelacanth is a good example of this.

Natural selection in action

The operation of natural selection can be seen in animals which are introduced to a new country and have to adapt to the new environment or perish. The varying hare was introduced from Norway into the Faroes in the 1860's, and in the harsh but snowless Faroes environment fewer and fewer of them turned white in winter. Today the whole population retains its summer colour all the year round. The 'new' race is called *Lepus timidus seclusus*. Natural selection can also be seen in animals whose environment changes around them. In the 1850's the Industrial Revolution blackened the trees around British cities, and lichen-coloured moths were no longer camouflaged; so a mutation whose bearers were black, and therefore camouflaged, spread, and today most of the moth population of the polluted woods are black, in sharp contrast with the same species of moth in unpolluted woods.

The first living things, roughly classified as single-celled plants, have been dated at 3 000 million years ago. The first animal life that has been found, existed 2 000 million years ago. By 500 million, animal life was flourishing and most of the major invertebrate groups were well established. Around 400 million we find the first evidence of vertebrates—extremely primitive fishes. Some fishes evolved 230 million years ago into amphibians, and the invasion of the land took place; 150 million years ago, mammals evolved, and about 70 million years ago, near the end of the great age of reptiles, we find a little creature called *Purgatorius*, which according to Sloan, Van

△ *A direct forerunner of man, proconsul man lived in Africa about 18 million years ago.*

Valen and Szalay was the first primate: the earliest member of the order to which man belongs.

The primates spread and diversified. The primitive forms, called prosimians (represented today by lemurs and tarsiers) have been found in Europe, Asia and North America, and from which arose the so-called higher primates, which developed somewhere in the Old World, and independently in South America, where such divergent species as the spider, howler, capuchin and squirrel monkeys evolved.

The first higher primates

In the Old World the first higher primates we know of have been found in the Fayûm, in Egypt, in deposits dated at 35 — 28 million years old. At about this time or a little later, the Old World higher primates were breaking away into two stocks: a four-legged monkey stock, whose living descendants are the baboons, macaques, guenons, colobus and langurs, and a hominoid stock, represented today by the apes and man. The small-sized *Aegyptopithecus*, whose remains are plentiful in the later Fayûm deposits, was certainly the 'daddy of us all'—whether he was also the daddy of the monkeys is a matter of dispute.

During the Miocene epoch—between 25 and 10 million years ago—apes of varying sizes seem to have become abundant. We blithely call them 'apes', but of course they were far less specialised creatures than the chimpanzee, gorilla, orang-utan and gibbon of today. First the gibbons' ancestors became distinct, then the line leading to the orang-utan. The creature *Ramapithecus*, living in East Africa and southern Asia about

12 million years ago, provides evidence that the ancestors of the African apes (gorilla and chimpanzee) and man had parted company to develop separately.

The importance of *Ramapithecus* was not fully grasped by specialists until, in a series of papers from about 1960 onwards, Dr Elwyn Simons of Yale showed that it had features of the jaws and teeth unmistakably foreshadowing those of man. The genus *Ramapithecus* had been originally described in 1935 on the evidence of some upper jaws from the Siwalik Hills in the Punjab; another genus, *Bramapithecus*, has been described on some mandibles from the same place. Dr Simons, by the simple expedient of fitting the upper and lower jaws together, showed that the two supposed genera were one and the same, and that the resultant creature made a very convincing ancestor for man!

Ramapithecus lived alongside the 'apes' which had given it birth, and were later to give rise to the gorilla and chimpanzee. But the heyday of the ape was nearing its close. Gradually, from about 12 million years ago onward, apes disappear from the fossil record. Some must have existed, because there are still some today, but their remains are scanty and dubious, and clearly they have long been as scarce as they are today. Instead, we find fossil monkeys. The teeth of Old World monkeys are very specialised, highly characteristic, and quite unmistakable; there is no doubt that, for some reason not yet clear, from about 12 million years ago almost to the present day, the monkeys have replaced the apes as the dominant type of primate in the Old World. We think of monkeys as more primitive than apes because they are less close to man: but this is only partially true.

Proto-men emerge

About two million years ago—very recently, geologically speaking—the ancestors of man, 'lying low' since *Ramapithecus* days, re-emerged. Their remains have been found in Olduvai Gorge in Tanzania by Dr Louis Leakey, in South Africa by Professor Raymond Dart and Dr Robert Broom, and at other sites, while the stone implements they made litter the ground at many sites in Asia and Africa, and later on in Europe too. Taking a broad view, these proto-men can be classified as *Australopithecus africanus*; but as far as we can tell they differ little from *Ramapithecus*. Of course, we cannot tell for sure, as we have not yet found limb bones of *Ramapithecus*; but those of *Australopithecus* are known, and we know that the creature walked upright on its back legs: not as fully or efficiently as modern man, it is true, but well on the way, in spite of the rather apelike skull.

From then on, the fossil story is clear. Every intermediate stage from *Australopithecus*, with its small brain and large teeth, to modern man, with his large brain and small teeth, is known. Aberrant types, like the wellknown Neanderthal man, arose, flourished briefly, and became extinct, but the line leading to modern man continued unbroken. Exactly when the racial differences within modern man became established is disputed. They are unimportant, however, in the overall picture.

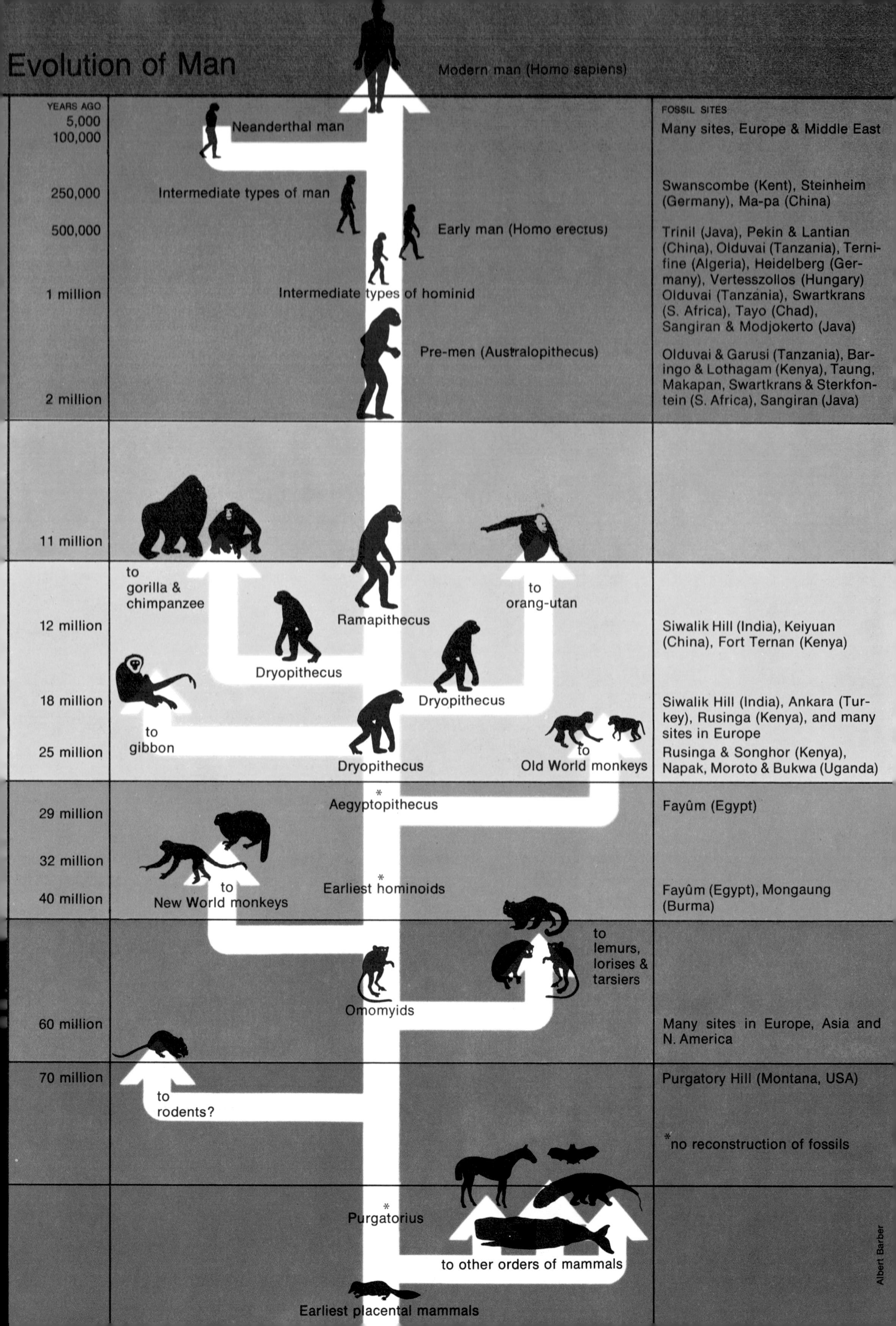

Evolution of Man

Modern man (Homo sapiens)

YEARS AGO		FOSSIL SITES
5,000 100,000	Neanderthal man	Many sites, Europe & Middle East
250,000	Intermediate types of man	Swanscombe (Kent), Steinheim (Germany), Ma-pa (China)
500,000	Early man (Homo erectus)	Trinil (Java), Pekin & Lantian (China), Olduvai (Tanzania), Terni-fine (Algeria), Heidelberg (Germany), Vertesszollos (Hungary)
1 million	Intermediate types of hominid	Olduvai (Tanzania), Swartkrans (S. Africa), Tayo (Chad), Sangiran & Modjokerto (Java)
2 million	Pre-men (Australopithecus)	Olduvai & Garusi (Tanzania), Baringo & Lothagam (Kenya), Taung, Makapan, Swartkrans & Sterkfontein (S. Africa), Sangiran (Java)
11 million	to gorilla & chimpanzee / Ramapithecus / to orang-utan	
12 million	Dryopithecus	Siwalik Hill (India), Keiyuan (China), Fort Ternan (Kenya)
18 million	Dryopithecus	Siwalik Hill (India), Ankara (Turkey), Rusinga (Kenya), and many sites in Europe
25 million	to gibbon / Dryopithecus / to Old World monkeys	Rusinga & Songhor (Kenya), Napak, Moroto & Bukwa (Uganda)
29 million	Aegyptopithecus *	Fayûm (Egypt)
32 million		
40 million	to New World monkeys / Earliest hominoids *	Fayûm (Egypt), Mongaung (Burma)
	to lemurs, lorises & tarsiers	
60 million	Omomyids	Many sites in Europe, Asia and N. America
70 million	to rodents?	Purgatory Hill (Montana, USA)
		*no reconstruction of fossils
	Purgatorius * / to other orders of mammals	
	Earliest placental mammals	

Albert Barber

Dinosaurs

The dinosaurs were the largest land animals that have lived on this earth. No man has ever seen one of these prehistoric monsters alive as they died out 70 million years ago. We can, however, deduce what they looked like and how they lived from the many fossils that have been found.

They first appeared in the Upper Triassic about 180 million years ago, as descendants of the thecodonts, reptiles that had teeth embedded in deep sockets, and they dominated the earth throughout the Jurassic and Cretaceous periods. This era of time, the Mesozoic, is often referred to now as the Age of Reptiles. During this time the land was lower than it is now and the oceans were larger and shallower. The climate was about the same but without the extremes of polar and tropical weather.

Most of the dinosaurs were huge creatures. Everything about them was of enormous proportions except their brains, their downfall in the long run. Some dinosaurs were small, smaller in fact than the largest living reptile, the Komodo dragon, and ranged in size down to that of a chicken.

The first fossil remains of a dinosaur were found by Dr and Mrs Mantell in 1822. Mantell identified some large teeth as belonging to an animal like the American lizard *Iguana*, and called this animal *Iguanodon*, 'iguana tooth'. The first dinosaur to be described was *Megalosaurus*, meaning 'large reptile', by Professor W Buckland in 1824. From many other fossils found since the last century we now know that the dinosaurs belonged to the Archosauria, of which the only living members are the crocodiles. By further examination of fossils it has been possible to separate the dinosaurs into two quite different groups, the 'reptile hips', the Saurischia, and the 'bird hips', the Ornithischia. But although we can identify and classify these extinct reptiles we can only guess at the reasons why they died out.

As they grew bigger some dinosaurs spent a lot of time in water, which helped buoy up their massive bodies. So they could reach a far greater size than animals that lived on land except that the females had to be able to walk onto land to lay their eggs.

The probable reason for their extinction is that they were unable to adapt themselves to the changing environmental conditions of the Cretaceous. But they must never be considered as failures; they ruled the earth for over 100 million years, which is 100 times longer than man has been in existence!

△ *An artist's reconstruction of* **Diplodocus**, *a giant saurischian dinosaur which flourished in Jurassic times—about 150 million years ago. It was the largest of all terrestrial vertebrates, reaching a length of 85 ft, but like so many of these monstrous creatures it was entirely herbivorous, and probably spent its time wading about in the shallows browsing on water plants.*

△ *An expert carefully chips away the rock from around the fossilized remains of one of the specimens at the Dinosaur Quarry Visitor Center, where finds are exhibited in situ.*

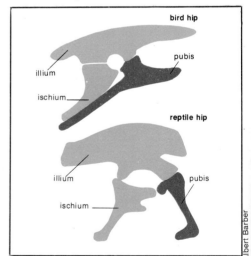

△ *Comparison of the pelvis of saurischians (below) with that of ornithischians (above), in which the pubis is directed backwards and bears an extra forward-pointing pre-pubic bone.*

◁ *The most well known of all the ornithopods, the herbivorous* Iguanodon *(reconstruction at far left, skeleton at left) roamed the lands in Jurassic and Cretaceous times. These creatures ran on their hind legs; some species reaching a length of about 31 ft and weighing several tons. Fossil remains of these dinosaurs were the first ever to be found, in 1822.*

Dinosaur Evolution

Thecodont ancestor. Both the saurischians and the ornithischians were descendants of the archosaurian thecodonts, which were in turn descendants of the cotylosaurs. During the Permian, the cotylosaurs branched into a number of varied lines, from the Triassic the reptiles flourished—the Age of Reptiles began.

Saurischia

Coelophysis, an early saurischian abundant in the late Triassic. There were two types of saurischians. *Coelophysis* was a bipedal flesh-eating theropod. Only a few feet long, it was one of the smallest dinosaurs with bird-like feet and well-developed hands and arms.

Tyrannosaurus, 'tyrant reptile', also a bipedal flesh-eating theropod alive at the end of the Cretaceous. It was the largest carnivore and weighed about 8 tons, stood about 18 ft high and could be 50 ft long.

Brontosaurus, a member of the other type of saurischians, the Sauropoda: quadrupedal plant-eaters, and the largest dinosaur weighing up to 30 tons. Apart from its minute brain it had an extra 'brain' in the pelvis acting as a booster for the hindlegs.

Ornithischia

Iguanodon, a herbivorous biped and a member of the Ornithopoda. Rare in the Triassic but abundant in the two later periods. The teeth of *Iguanodon* were the first dinosaur fossils to be found. It stood about 14 ft high and was about 31 ft long and must have looked something like a massive kangaroo.

Trachodon, an ornithopod with a duck-like beak and bird-like feet. Some duckbills also developed crest-like outgrowths of the skull. The ornithischians had no front teeth but their back teeth were massed like a mosaic, with a total of up to 2000 in some duckbills; good equipment for a diet of tubers and horsetails.

Stegosaurus, 'plated reptile', an armoured dinosaur. All armoured dinosaurs were herbivorous and quadrupedal and very slow creatures. Their armour helped to defend them against the carnivorous theropods. *Stegosaurus* had two rows of triangular plates along its back and tail.

Ankylosaurus, also armoured but with a complete covering of broad bony plates. Like a living 'tank', it only had to crouch to the ground to defend itself. It was 5 ft wide, 5 ft high and 16 ft long.

Triceratops, a horned dinosaur, one of the last to survive. This 30 ft reptile just had to stand firmly on its feet with head well down and 3 ft long horns pointing forward to fend off any predator. A herd would send any *Tyrannosaurus* running!

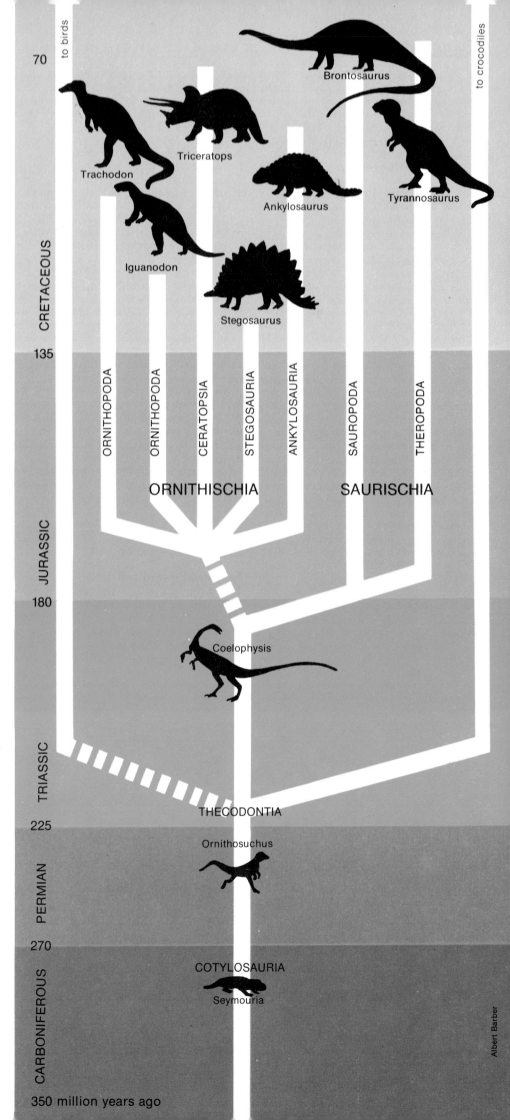

Albert Barber

Evolution in action

It is a general rule that the older the world has become the more complex are the systems that have evolved. This applies equally to living and non-living things. On the one hand chemical changes between less than 100 elements, eventually led to the amino-acids and proteins; on the other hand, over a million different species of living creatures have arisen during the last 1 000 million years. The simplest forms of life no doubt competed at the earliest times in 'the soupy sea of amino-acids'.

Life has always been competitive and subject to laws and discipline. Because of this, animals and plants have succeeded in colonising practically the whole of the world's surfaces—from the deepest oceans to the hottest springs and the furthermost caves. In these three extremes the environment has changed but little in the last 50 million years and so we can see today the stability of species in such circumstances. Mutation (and recombination between, say, ten thousand different genes per species) have not produced a more efficient organism under the conditions imposed today than the earlier 'model'. The coelacanth *Malania* fish is a good example of this. I attended the presentation of *Malania* to the Prime Minister of South Africa by the late Professor JLB Smith and I could examine *Malania* closely. Its appearance varies little from the fossilised forebears which occurred 50 million years ago. The waters around the Comores have remained unchanged. The 'ultimate defence' of the coelacanth is, I think, its horrible, foulsmelling oil. Maybe, like the hydrogen bomb of today, this has succeeded as the great deterrent to attack throughout time.

Such examples are rare and over most of the earth's surfaces changes take place gradually, rarely rapidly. If every point on earth had maintained a constant and identical environment, evolution could not have taken place; such a uniform situation would have led to complete stability with fixed universal species. The *changes* in the environment have led to the multitude of ecological niches which are offered and each of these has been exploited fully today. Such changes have usually been gradual, as for example, between the Ice Ages. Species then have advanced, retracted or become isolated and modified over tens of thousands of years.

Man upsets nature's balance

Until the advent of man, nature was in balance. In the past 1—3 thousand years, man has upset this balance—in two ways.

First, by changing the world's environment. Second, by his unique contribution—psycho-social evolution—a short-cut method of passing on knowledge; not by a genetic code, but by ritualisation of past experience.

We are here concerned with the first of these: man's recent effect on the environment. We must face the fact that he has polluted the air, the rivers and even the oceans, and all living things have had to adjust to new situations. We have, therefore, been given opportunities to see how rapidly nature has been able to adapt. The alternative has been, and is, extinction.

Air pollution, except smoke from forest fires and volcanic eruptions, began during the Industrial Revolution, towards the end of the 18th century.

It has been my particular line of enquiry to research into its effects on living things today. Since around 1800, home and factory chimneys have been belching forth, day and night, smoke particles whose fall-out near source may amount to 50 tons per square mile per month, as in Sheffield. The lighter particles may travel over a thousand miles on the prevailing wind.

Industrial melanism

The toxic effects of air pollution have blackened the ground itself and killed the lichens on tree trunks and boughs. These are the normal resting places by day of large numbers of camouflaged or 'cryptic' moths. Many species which in the past had developed lichen-patterns today find themselves exposed on blackened tree trunks. Had they been unable to adapt they would now be extinct except in the remotest areas of the world. However, this has not happened: black forms have replaced the earlier light ones.

By large-scale laboratory and field experiments we have shown that these black forms have existed at a low frequency in the past, but that they have spread from being extreme rarities (say one in 1 000) to 95% in many populations of different species in and around industrial areas today. We have proved that this is largely due to the effects of natural selection under intensive visual predation: that bird predators eliminate 30% more of the conspicuous form than of the camouflaged one. In under 100 years (an incredibly short time) these insects have been able to adapt to a new coloration demanded by a new situation. This is the most striking evolutionary change ever to have been witnessed by man, and it is referred to as 'industrial melanism'.

In the majority of instances these new black forms are controlled by a single gene and black is dominant to light. That is to say, when black mates with light either 50% or 100% of the offspring will be black, according to the constitution of the black parents (heterozygote or homozygote).

So great a change in coloration affects many other characteristics in the melanic individuals which are controlled by the same gene and adjustments have to be made throughout the gene-complex (the sum total of genes controlling all aspects of the individual's life). There are, in fact, physiological, behavioural and chemical differences between the black and light forms.

In Britain alone, over 100 species of moths have changed in this way and industrial melanism is widespread also in North America and throughout Europe, but so far has not been found in the tropics. This, then, is the indirect effect of smoke pollution on Lepidoptera.

Other pollutants are being met in the same way by nature. Mosquitoes have become resistant to DDT; rats will tolerate the poison, warfarin. In each instance the resistant forms are favoured by natural selection and resistant animals are established.

This is evolution occurring today.

◁ *Light form of the oak beauty moth perfectly camouflaged against a lichen-covered tree trunk. As the toxic effects of air pollution blackened the trees and killed the lichen, the light forms became conspicuous and were picked off. The dark form now predominates in Britain.*

▽ *Easily seen against a branch blackened by pollution, a light form of the peppered moth falls an easy victim to a redstart.*

HBD Kettlewell

Bird speciation

Birds are the best-known of any class of animals. There are only 8 000 species and there cannot be many unknown ones, though occasional new discoveries are made in such places as New Guinea, tropical Africa and tropical South America. More is known of their life histories than of most other animals', largely because, like ourselves, they are mostly diurnal animals whose chief sense organ is the eye. Thus their lives are more easily studied and their behaviour more easily understood than is the case with other vertebrate groups, let alone the invertebrates.

Because rather few fossil birds are known, and birds as a whole are structurally rather uniform, the evolution of the major groups of birds is not very well understood; but a good deal is known about the origin of new species and subspecies, and many of the principles that have been worked out in birds probably apply equally to other animals.

The steps which lead to the splitting of one species into two are basically quite simple. First, the original species is divided into two isolated parts. This may happen in a variety of ways: climatic change may isolate the populations in two separate 'areas with an unsuitable habitat in between; or the formation of a mountain range may have the same effect; or one species may colonise an island or a new continent, and so be isolated from the parent stock by sea.

Once isolation has been achieved, in whatever way it may be, the two populations will tend each to become adapted to local conditions which will almost certainly not be identical. Gradually, genetic differences will be built up in the two stocks. These will show differences in appearance, habits, song, and so on. The crucial step in species formation may then follow. If the barrier between the two stocks breaks down and they come together again, it may turn out that they have diverged sufficiently to keep separate. They may either not interbreed at all, or if they occasionally do they will produce hybrids which may be ill-adapted and will not persist. There is reason to believe that natural selection will tend to increase the original differences between the two new species and competition between them will be minimised. With increasing divergence in the ways in which the two related species fit into their habitat will probably go increased divergence in their appearance and behaviour.

Case histories

In some cases the history of species formation can be reconstructed in some detail. Thus the European treecreepers consist of two very similar species. Their ranges overlap widely, but one, the short-toed treecreeper, has a more westerly distribution than the other, the common treecreeper, which ranges east across Siberia. It seems almost certain that during one of the Pleistocene ice ages less than 2 million years ago, the original treecreeper stock was split and isolated in eastern and western 'forest refuges'; when milder conditions returned and the forest spread back and became con-

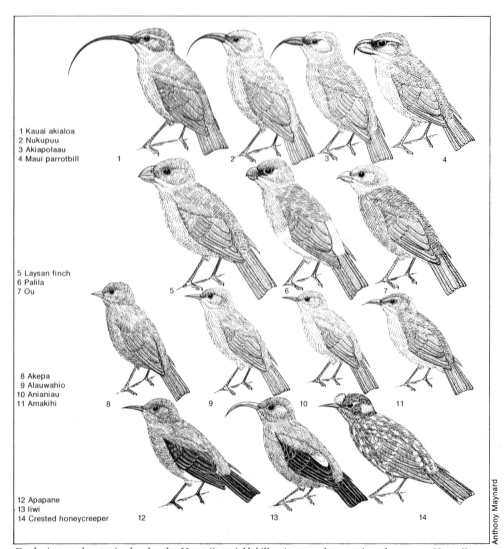

1 Kauai akialoa
2 Nukupuu
3 Akiapolaau
4 Maui parrotbill
5 Laysan finch
6 Palila
7 Ou
8 Akepa
9 Alauwahio
10 Anianiau
11 Amakihi
12 Apapane
13 Iiwi
14 Crested honeycreeper

Anthony Maynard

Evolution at the species level—the Hawaiian sicklebills. At an unknown time the remote Hawaiian Islands were colonised by birds, probably finches, from the Americas. They gave rise to a whole new family, containing some remarkably unfinchlike forms. Some 22 species, of which 8 are now extinct, evolved from the original stock by adaptive radiation. The surviving 14 are illustrated, showing bills adapted for everything from nectar-sipping and nut-cracking to grubbing beetles from trees.

tinuous across Europe and Siberia, the two treecreeper stock probably met again and had acquired sufficient differences to maintain themselves as two separate species. They are not very different to look at, but their songs differ, and song, so closely integrated into breeding behaviour, is an important 'isolating mechanism' in birds.

The formation of any new species results in a new type, adapted to exploit in a new way some combination of the varied resources offered by the environment. Thus with the multiplication of bird species the environment is, so to speak, more and more finely parcelled out. This happened on every continent a very long time ago, and we take for granted the great array of predators, scavengers, insect-eaters, seed-eaters—and in the tropics fruit-eaters and nectar-eaters—each with a structure and behaviour beautifully adapted to its particular 'niche'. But this process—adaptive radiation, as it is usually called—is most clearly seen on some isolated archipelagos, where an original colonist has in the absence of other birds undergone a spectacular adaption of its own, resulting in the evolution of a number of new forms quite different from the original stock in appearance and habits.

Darwin's finches

The most famous example is from the Galapagos Islands in the Pacific Ocean, where Charles Darwin, on his voyage round the world, noticed the structural diversity of the finches, which from their plumage, nests and other characters seemed clearly to be descended from the same stock. Darwin's finches, as they are now known, in fact provided one of the most important clues which ultimately led him to his theory of evolution. Almost certainly the original colonist, a small finch-like bird, found the islands vegetated but practically—or perhaps entirely—devoid of land-birds. Over the ages the original stock has given rise to birds with fine beaks like warblers which eat insects, birds with strong parrot-like beaks for cracking hard seeds, birds with pointed beaks which probe flowers for insects and honey, and has even produced a woodpecker finch, which has not evolved the woodpecker's long tongue but instead makes use of a cactus spine or fine twig to probe for grubs in dead wood.

The main principles of species formation are not difficult to understand; but the variations are countless, and it is among the birds that some of the most fascinating examples of variety are to be found.

Genetics of the black panther

The big cats, lion, tiger, leopard, jaguar and snow leopard, are one of the main attractions at a zoo. Most visitors will probably recall seeing the majestic leopard and black panther, probably in adjoining cages. What is perhaps not widely known is that the black panther is just a black variety of the spotted leopard, in the same manner as the black domestic cat is a variety of the tabby.

The reason why blackness in the panther is so common, as compared with blackness in other animals, is that the colour occurs at a high frequency in areas of tropical or semi-tropical rain forests, a habitat in which it can apparently flourish and compete with the normal spotted leopard. Just why it can survive so successfully is not known with certainty but one explanation could be that the black colour provides an excellent camouflage in the gloom of the forest. In more open country, the spotted leopard is the dominant form. In much of Burma, Malaysia, and Thailand the black panther is common and many specimens in captivity have either originated from these countries or have descended from animals which once lived in them.

Zoo breedings

Both the leopard and the black panther will breed in zoos. Furthermore, they will interbreed and produce fertile offspring. This is one proof that the two animals belong to the same species. Considering the large number of years in which the black form has been bred in captivity, it might be thought that the heredity of the colour was well known. Surprisingly, this is not so, and for several reasons. One is that the leopard is not a quick breeding species although, once sexually mature, it will persistently produce litters of about two cubs for many years. The record seems to be a total of 22 young over a period of 8 years, and this will probably be surpassed. Another reason is that the black panther commands a higher price than the ordinary leopard, so most pairings are between black animals, not between spotted and black. Again, few zoo directors can support a leopard breeding programme for the number of years which would be required to establish the mode of heredity.

This does not mean, however, that the problem could not be tackled. Crosses between the spotted and black form are occasionally undertaken and mixed litters of spotted and black cubs are often seen. This shows that the colour difference is certainly inherited. That is, the cubs are either spotted, or black, not a dark spotted animal as might be thought. The black colour is thus inherited in a simple Mendelian fashion. But the question remains whether black is dominant or recessive to spotted. Unfortunately, it is not always easy to answer such questions if systematic crosses cannot be carried out. Some authorities have speculated that the black colour would be inherited as a dominant while others have thought it would behave as a recessive. The breeding data commonly available are too meagre and, in general, fail to yield firm conclusions.

Leopard questionnaire

It was decided in 1968 to try and answer this question by canvassing throughout the world zoos known to be breeding leopards. The outcome could have been indefinite, of course, but, at least, the replies could furnish some interesting data on the breeding of leopards and, at best, provide a solution to the long standing problem. In all 128 zoos were circulated with a suitably phrased enquiry on their breeding experiences with leopards. Of these, 65 (51%) supplied useful information. Without delving into technicalities, it was discovered that the black variety is inherited as a simple recessive to the spotted. For example, pairings of black with black invariably gave black offspring while spotted with spotted often gave all spotted but occasionally spotted and black. This is conclusive evidence, especially as mixed litters are given by different parents.

But when the numbers of cubs born per litter to the black mothers were compared with those born to the spotted mothers, it was noticed that the average number was smaller. Black mothers give birth to an average litter of 1·8 cubs while the spotted mother has an average of 2·1. The difference between these averages may not seem to be great but the amount of data from which these are derived is sufficient for the difference to be taken seriously. The implication, therefore, is that the black panther does not reproduce quite so prolifically as the ordinary leopard. Various explanations could be offered for the lower fecundity. Perhaps the panther mother does not take so kindly to the stresses imposed by captivity so her breeding ability is upset.

On the other hand, the lower fecundity could be due to the mutant gene which produces the black colour. It is by no means uncommon for mutant genes to affect the fertility of those individuals which carry them. This possibility points towards an interesting speculation. In parts of southwest continental Asia, the spotted and black colours constitute a polymorphism, a term used by zoologists to describe a population in which two distinct forms are co-existent and freely interbreed yet neither one completely displaces the other. An advantage in the form of superior concealment could perhaps explain how the black variety has become common despite its disadvantage of lower fertility, which has in turn prevented it from finally ousting the spotted. It is thus possible that the present work has uncovered a negative factor which is preventing the black variety from displacing the spotted. In any event, the possibility could act as a stimulus for further work. The importance of this survey is that it enabled world zoos to contribute to scientific knowledge, and proved that they have a more serious part to play than the mere exhibiting of exotic animals.

◁ A puzzle for zoo visitors: panther and leopard are not as different as they seem. Though they may be in separate cages they are one and the same animal, and will interbreed freely. Breeding experiments have shown that the leopard's spotted coat is the result of a simply-inherited gene whose effect is dominant over that of the gene for black coat. The diagram on the next page explains its inheritance.

◁ The panther is a black or melanic variety of the leopard species, arising when the 'normal' gene for a spotted coat is absent. Pure-bred leopards mated with pure-bred panthers produce only spotted young, but on average one in four of the offspring of these hybrid young will be black. Melanic forms are also encountered from time to time among other members of the cat family, such as the well known and beautiful jaguar of South America.

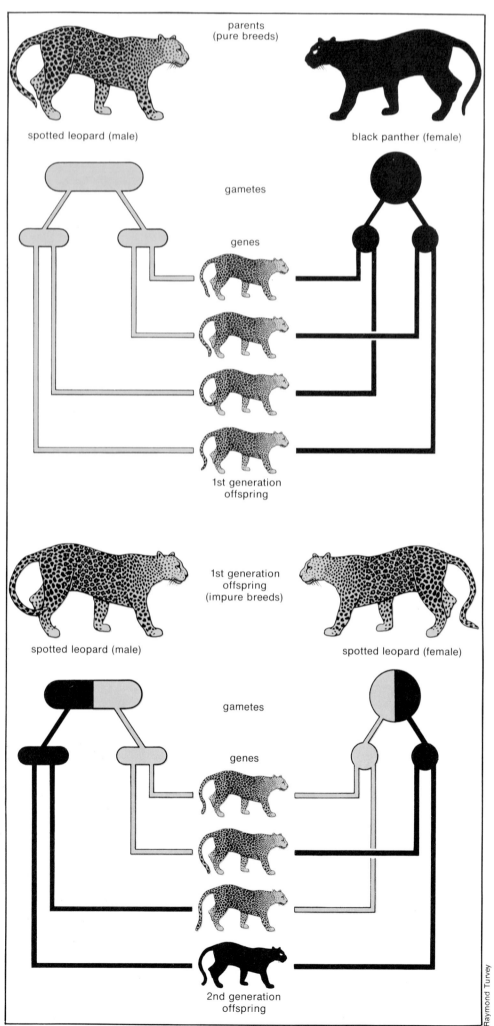

parents
(pure breeds)

spotted leopard (male)

black panther (female)

gametes

genes

1st generation
offspring

1st generation
offspring
(impure breeds)

spotted leopard (male)

spotted leopard (female)

gametes

genes

2nd generation
offspring

Raymond Turvey

The mechanism of inheritance

Heredity is the transmission of characteristics from one generation to the next. This statement is summed up neatly in the old proverb that says 'like begets like'. Genetics is the study of the inheritance of these characteristics and all the laws that govern them. What is handed on from parent to offspring is the capacity for the offspring to acquire these characteristics.

It was the great biologist Gregor Mendel who made the first essential steps in the study of heredity. From the hundreds of experiments Mendel did he came to two conclusions which he expressed as two laws. Mendel's first law is the 'Law of Segregation' and says that genes are present in pairs and when an individual forms gametes, that is eggs or spermatozoa, no gamete contains more than one member of any pair. Applying this law to the case of the black panther it means that when a pure-bred male spotted leopard is mated with a pure-bred female black panther, the leopard will form one type of sperm containing a single gene for spotted coat, and the panther will form one type of egg containing a single gene for black coat. This is shown in the top illustration. When mated a sperm carrying the gene for spotted coat can unite only with an egg carrying the gene for black coat, so all the cubs carry both types of genes. But they all have spotted coats. This happens because the gene for spotted coat is known from other crosses to be dominant over the gene for black coat. The offspring are impure breeds as they have unlike genes controlling the coat colour.

When two offspring interbreed, as shown in the bottom illustration, the male spotted leopard forms two types of sperm, one carrying the gene for spotted coat the other for black coat. The egg of the female spotted leopard acts in similar fashion. At fertilisation there is a random meeting of the sperm with the egg, as the diagram shows, so there are three possible combinations of genes in the offspring. A cub may have two genes for spotted coat, a pure breed of spotted leopard, or one gene for spotted and one for black coat, an impure breed of spotted leopard, or two genes for black coat, a pure breed of black panther. Again when the two different genes are present the cub will have a spotted coat because this is the dominant character, but when the two genes for black coat are present the cub will be a pure-bred black panther. So this explains how when two spotted leopards mate there may be, surprisingly, a black panther in the litter.

These illustrations are purely diagrammatic, as they assume that in each litter there are four offspring and each offspring shows a certain gene combination. This does not happen of course every time leopards mate, but if the parents' coat colour, the cubs' coat colour and the number of cubs in each litter are recorded over a number of years then the same results will be achieved as those shown.

This is an example of the 3:1 ratio of monohybrid inheritance, the inheritance of one pair of genes, where 75% of the offspring show the dominant character, in this case spotted coat, and 25% show the recessive character, black coat.

Albinism

Animal colours are achieved in two ways: structurally and through the presence of pigments. Structural colours are due to the interference, diffraction and scattering of light on the animal's surface. Pigmentary colours are due to the presence of coloured pigments in the cells.

Albinism is the absence of melanin, the main pigment that gives eyes and skin and its derivatives, their colour. An albino animal is instantly recognisable by three distinctive features: white hair, feathers or scales, reddish-white skin and pink eyes. The reddish tinge of the skin is due to the effect of tiny blood vessels showing through superficial skin layers. The eyes are pink for the same reason, as the blood vessels are not hidden by any pigment in the iris.

Melanin is a black pigment usually found in the form of granules, contained in cells called melanophores. The rapid colour change effected by some cold-blooded animals is due to the dispersion of pigment granules into the branches, or the grouping of the granules in the middle of each chromatophore. In mammals and birds, both warm-blooded animals in which there are no such quick colour changes, the branched pigment cells are smaller and called melanocytes. It is not known if the melanin granules move in the melanocytes.

To understand why albino animals occur we must go back to the first stages of melanin production. Melanin synthesis was discovered in 1895 when Bourquelot and Bertrand found that a colourless substance in a toadstool is blackened by an enzyme present in the fungus. Bertrand later recognised the substance as the amino acid tyrosine and Bourquelot named the enzyme tyrosinase. It was Biedermann who two years later discovered tyrosinase in an animal. Thus melanin is formed from tyrosine by the action of the enzyme tyrosinase. Since these early studies it has been found that the various biochemical steps in the synthesis of melanin are gene-controlled. The first step involves the conversion of tyrosine by tyrosinase. One gene, the albino gene, blocks the production of tyrosinase, so no melanin is formed. When there is a double dose of this abnormal and recessive gene an animal exhibits albinism.

Variations of albinism

Albinism is therefore hereditary. There is a series of albino genes which control the intensity of hair, eye, and skin pigmentation. This means that it is possible to breed animals with varying amounts of melanin. In cats, for example, one set of albino genes gives the so-called Siamese colour which is highly prized by cat fanciers. In rabbits there is another form of albinism known as Himalayan albinism. Himalayans have pink eyes and white fur except for their feet, tails, ears and the tips of their noses, which are black or dark brown. These examples are not true albinos as some melanin is present, but they show varying degrees of albinism. Partial albinism shows as a piebald type. The mildest, and most familiar, partial albino condition is found in man, and is known as the 'white forelock' which refers to the patch of white hair above the centre of the forehead. Mock-albinos, another form of albinism, can be produced in mice by the action of two mutant genes, one removing the pigment from hair, the other from eyes. The only difference in external appearance from a true albino animal is that the eyes of a mock-albino are much smaller than normal.

Melanin acts as a light screen protecting the eyes and skin from the harmful rays in sunlight. An albino animal is at a disadvantage for it has impaired vision and is particularly conspicuous, easily preyed upon and may not be readily recognised by its own species. Like other pigments melanin has been involved through natural selection in the development of behaviour patterns. The albino gene is rarely of evolutionary advantage, for animals use their colours to identify themselves to their own kind, to attract a mate and to warn off would-be predators. Also animal coloration is a good means of hiding from enemies. Albino animals are relatively rare but wherever they occur they are never missed because they are so obvious. Albinism exists in almost every animal group, including man, where it appears in one out of 20 000 births.

▽ *Quite a contrast: 'Snowflake', a rare baby albino gorilla, with a companion at the Barcelona zoo. The young gorilla has unpigmented skin and hair but has blue eyes. Not only does he look special but he also seems to require more affection from his keeper than the other baby gorillas.*

Popperfoto

△ *A herd of albino red deer. Great respect is sometimes attached to albino animals; in parts of California white deerskins are prized trophies.*

▽ *Instantly recognisable albino: white-scaled, pink-eyed female albino molly and the normal male together with a male lyretail.*

▽ *Contrast in frogs: an albino common frog stands out against its background—which includes a well-concealed edible frog.*

Klaus Paysan

Geoffrey Kinns: AFA

Adaptation and longevity

The animal world is in a constant state of change; species existing today represent the level to which they have adapted to survive. Colour, whether for concealment, warning, or sheer bluff, is only one of the millions of adaptations necessary for this process, yet it is among the most obvious and spectacular. In no group of animals is this more obvious than in the insects; in this chapter they provide examples of most of the uses of colour. Special attention is given to some of the poisonous ones because of the extraordinary relationship between colour and poison. Basically, if an insect is unpalatable, it advertises this by bright colours. Any predator will learn to associate these markings with unpleasant experiences after only one of two attempts to eat the insect. Thus, for a small loss in population, some insects are protected by their colour. Other, completely palatable species, often of different families, have derived advantage from acquiring these colours and sharing equal immunity to predation.

If colour be one of the logical aspects of the animal kingdom, then relative longevity must be its opposite. Life spans vary, it seems, almost at random, and provide an interesting enigma — what, if anything, decides how long an animal can, not will, live?

Flight, the adaptation by which animals conquered the air, was a constant source of envy and mystery to man until relatively few years ago; here its mechanics are explained, and its application to the various classes of animal that have mastered it.

More subtle adaptations exist, however. In the world of insects, their very life-histories are adaptations to the maximum exploitation of food supplies and efficiency of dispersal. In the higher insects, the larvae exploit the best food source available in the habitat.

Protective coloration

All the colours of the rainbow can be seen in the millions of animal species. Many have coloured markings to identify themselves to their own kind, as in the guenon monkeys. In others the sexes have different colours, the male often being brilliantly coloured to attract a mate, as seen in the peacock or stickleback. In many species, however, the colours and patterns are to protect them.

A large number of animals are inconspicuous because their colours match the surroundings. This concealment or cryptic coloration is most effective and is often found in nature.

Some cicadas (bugs) of East Africa have colours and forms that closely resemble flowers. It is remarkable that they have the habit of bunching together, so looking like a floral inflorescence. One species has two coloured forms, a green and a yellow. These two morphs sit close together on vertical stems, with the green individuals at the top resembling buds and the yellow ones below looking like the opened flowers. This mimicry is so efficient that even experienced botanists have found themselves holding a bare stem after plucking a 'flower'.

Many animals with cryptic coloration, especially insects, have a second line of defence if attacked. Some moths and butterflies have eye-spots, looking like big vertebrate eyes, which are suddenly exposed by moving the second pair of wings. The eyed hawk moth will perform this beautifully for anyone who gives it a 'dig' when it is at rest. These huge eyes cause any small bird to flee immediately. Some moths, cryptic at rest, expose bright markings rather than eye-spots when disturbed which leaves the attacker confused as the moth becomes conspicuous one second and then disappears the next. When one studies a zebra it is hard to find a reason why it has such a flashy pyjama suit (below). It baffles scientists even today and several views are held. In the shade of a tree a zebra's dramatic stripes do give concealment. Close to a zebra herd, the stripes break up the animal's outline so a predator, such as a lion, cannot tell where one zebra ends and the next begins. When he springs to attack his judgement may be wrong and the zebra has time to escape. This is known as disruptive coloration. Another view is that the stripes exaggerate the size of the animal so again the attacker may miss when he jumps. Many animals accentuate their conspicuousness by being brightly coloured as seen in coral snakes, gila monsters and caterpillars (opposite). Again, this is subject to imitation. Many harmless moths derive protection from looking like inedible species, and only the experienced can tell true from false coral snakes.

Aligned confusion: a zebra's stripes probably serve to break up the body outline, making it difficult for a predator to focus on a single individual.

Disrupt to disguise: the garden carpet moth (right) **Xanthroe fluctuata** *shows the concealment effect of a disruptive pattern, having some parts which blend in with the background, while others differ strongly from it. The gecko (below) combines cryptic and disruptive coloration to help disguise itself against the tree trunk. Another means of defence is that it can shed its tail (by a process called autotomy) when it is attacked and so escape capture.*

Blend and bluff: many animals gain protection by imitating their surroundings. The angle shades moth **Phlogophora meticulosa** *(below) with folded wings, head crest and mottled patterns gives excellent concealment among dead leaves. Many insects such as grasshoppers, moths and stick insects have adapted to resemble growing twigs. The New Zealand prickly stick insect* **Acanthoxyla prasina** *(right) shows a cryptic coloration resting attitude on a bramble bush.*

Eat me at your peril: the bright colours of the spurge moth caterpillar (below) warn predators that it is unpalatable. Warning patterns of animals include red, yellow, black and white—all colours that stand out well. All are used to good effect in this handsome specimen. On a fern frond, bird dropping or spider? A crab spider successfully mimics a bird dropping (below right). This technique is unusual; most crab spider species match to perfection the flowers on which they lurk.

Colours of animals

When daylight falls on a white animal, the different parts of the light spectrum (all the wavelengths) are reflected, giving our eyes the impression of whiteness. When the animal is coloured, on the other hand, some of the wavelengths of the light falling on it are reflected whilst others are absorbed by the outer covering (hair, feathers, or hide) of the animal. So the colour of an animal is due to the removal by absorption of some of the wavelengths in the light incident on its external surface.

There are two principal methods by which wavelengths can be absorbed; by the physical nature of the reflecting surface, giving what are known as structural colours, or by pigments giving their own colours. In some cases an animal's colour is due to a combination of the two.

Structural colours

Structural colours are due either to interference or to the scattering of light. When a layer of oil spreads out on the surface of the water, interference colours can be seen: the colour of the oil changes with the angle of vision. The same effect can be seen in the iridescent feathers of a starling or humming-bird, and in certain beetles. The structure of an iridescent feather 'interferes' with the light striking it.

The other kind of structural colour, which does not change with the position of the observer's eye, is due to the scattering of light. The shorter waves in white light are scattered by extremely small particles. This kind of structural colour is responsible for the blue of the sky and the blue on a jay's wing; in neither case is a blue pigment present. In blue feathers the scattering units are actually minute air spaces in the solid keratin (the protein of which feathers are made). These are rather special cases, for most animal colours are due to the presence of chemical pigments.

Pigment colours

Perhaps the commonest animal pigment is melanin, which usually appears in the form of very insoluble granules. Melanin is made of various types of protein pigment; the colours presented depend on various conditions. It colours dark hair, fur, and skin, black feathers, black slugs and many other animals. The ink of octopus and cuttlefish is almost pure melanin. Sometimes melanin occurs in a brown or reddish-brown form and these colours can be seen in many mammals and in birds such as female pheasants.

Some of the brighter animal colours are produced by the pigments known as carotenoids which give red, orange and yellow colours. These pigments are of plant origin and they enter an animal's body in its food. The simplest is carotene, found in carrots. Most animals can join two molecules of carotene to make vitamin A. Carotenoids produce the reds and browns of sea-stars, the yellow of egg yolk and many other similar colours. A live lobster is blue; this colour is due to a combination of red carotenoid with a protein. When a lobster is boiled, the increase in heat causes the bond to break, leaving the red colour seen in a lobster offered for sale.

Food gives pink colour

The pink colour of flamingoes is due to another carotenoid which the bird obtains from its natural food. In zoos, flamingoes often lose their beautiful pink tone because they are fed on a diet lacking in carotenoid; the colour can be restored if the flamingoes are given food such as shrimps that contains carotenoid.

Melanins and carotenoids are very widespread in the animal kingdom, but some pigments have a very limited distribution. For instance, many sea-urchins have reddish or purplish colours which are due to naphthaquinone pigments. These are complicated organic compounds which are deposited in the hard spines and shell of the sea-urchin. The related anthraquinone pigments occur in some insects. The best known is cochineal, a red pigment in the body of the tropical American bug *Dactylopius cacti*. Cochineal is the basis of carmine which is used as a food colorant and watercolour pigment; it is also used in cosmetics, and the Aztecs dyed their cloth with it.

The pigment turacin has an even more restricted distribution, for it is found only in the red feathers of the turacos or Musophagidae, a family of tropical birds sometimes known as plantain-eaters. Turacin is a porphyrin combined with copper. Porphyrins without a metal occur in many other animals—some sea-stars, for example, molluscs, the shells of birds' eggs, and owl and bustard feathers—but here they do not contribute greatly to the coloration.

Tyrian purple is another rare pigment which is found only in a small gland in the dog-whelk *Nucella lapillus* and its relatives in the family Muricidae. In Roman times this pigment was extracted from the molluscs by boiling the whole animal. The resulting brew was used to dye the robes of emperors giving the colour known as imperial purple.

Not all the yellow, orange and red colours are produced by carotenoids. Some are due to pterins, such as xanthopterin, the yellow pigment of the brimstone butterfly. Pterins are also found in fishes, amphibians and reptiles; the pigment cells of goldfish contain both carotenoids and pterins.

Combined colours

Many animal colours are due to the combination of two or more pigments or of a pigment and a structural colour. A good example of the latter is the plumage of the tropical magpie *Cissa*, in which the feathers have a structure that scatters light overlaid by a layer of yellow pigment (probably carotenoid). The combination of a scattering structure (giving blue) and yellow pigment produces green feathers. When living in forests *Cissa* is usually green, but in open country this bird is blue, probably because the yellow pigment has been bleached in the light, leaving behind the blue structure.

The colours of animals can, therefore, be produced in many different ways and it is never wise to assume that one colour is always associated with one pigment. There is, in fact, much scope for further research into this interesting subject—with its inherent beauty as a bonus.

△ *Presence or absence of the pigment melanin dictates the whites, browns, and blacks of horses' hair.*
▷ *The feather structure of the peacock disrupts light waves, causing an iridescent sheen.*
▽ *Combination: the blue of the macaw is derived from light absorption by feather structure, the black from melanin pigment, and the white results from total reflection of all light waves.*

2714

Poisonous butterflies and moths

The fact that butterflies and moths (Lepidoptera) may contain poisonous substances in their body tissues is a relatively new discovery. Only ten years ago Karl Jordan, one of the greatest entomologists of his time, commenting on this possibility, wrote authoritatively: 'The garden tiger moth, in its adult stage, is a completely harmless insect.' It is now known that this moth (*Arctia caja* L.) secretes a toxic substance (*ββ* dimethylacrylylcholine) in its defensive glands; that the burnet moths and foresters (Zygaenids) release cyanide (HCN) from their body tissues when crushed; that the cinnabar moth (*Callimorpha jacobaeae* L.) contains poisonous alkaloids (senecio alkaloids) plus a heavy concentration of histamine; the monarch butterfly (*Danaus plexippus* L.) stores heart poisons (cardenolides) in its haemolymph (blood); and that certain swallowtail butterflies (*Papilio*) ingest and store a poisonous acid (aristolochic acid) in their bodies.

Butterflies and moths have many enemies. They are attacked on the wing, for instance, by birds, bats, hornets, robberflies, dragonflies and other large insects, and when at rest, by birds, monkeys, lemurs, mice and various other small mammals, mantids and similar insects.

The poisonous substances in their bodies are part of their defence mechanisms—they produce a repellent taste or vile smell (or both) and local irritation of the mucous membranes of the predator, or if ingested may cause severe pain or discomfort after they have been swallowed. Thus, for example, a jay vomits violently about 10–15 minutes after swallowing the monarch butterfly. This is because the heart poisons in the body tissues of the butterfly also act upon the stomach, causing contraction of smooth muscle and the regurgitation of the meal. Two monarch butterflies contain enough heart poisons, if retained by the bird, to kill a starling.

Warning coloration

Bright colours and warning coloration are often associated with defence mechanisms of these types. Thus butterflies and moths armed with chemical repellents are often extremely conspicuous both in appearance and behaviour. If an inexperienced predator captures such a specimen it will receive a sharp lesson. It will associate these disagreeable qualities with the brilliant colour of the insect and in future keep at a safe distance. Expressed differently, it pays these insects to advertise their presence and the first victim is sacrificed for the future protection of the population.

The great naturalists of the 19th century had observed that a number of species of butterflies which were avoided by bird predators fed on poisonous plants, and deduced correctly that some of their repellent qualities were derived from their larval food. Thus certain swallowtails feed on birthwort and its allies (*Aristolochia*) and the monarch butterfly and its relatives on the poisonous milkweeds (*Asclepias*).

In the course of time they have evolved a

△ *Only in recent years have certain butterflies and moths been found to contain poisonous substances. The two monarch butterflies seen above store enough heart poisons (cardenolides) to kill a starling.*

method of extracting and storing these toxins and using them for their own protection. Their relationship with poisonous plants, however, involves another probably more important aspect. Eggs and young larvae laid or hatching on such foliage avoid destruction because the large herbivores do not feed upon these poisonous plants. Even hungry camels in the desert avoid *Asclepias*. The burnet moth larvae which feed on clovers and vetches that contain cyanide are thus protected from grazing rabbits, which are known to avoid these strains of the plants. The period in an insect's life when natural selection acts most severely is in the very early stages. Hundreds of eggs may be laid by one moth but the majority of the caterpillars hatching from them die when they are still tiny. An immense advantage must be conferred on a species with a food supply so noxious that other animals avoid it, and which consequently not only has more to eat, but is not itself accidentally eaten by grazing herbivores. It is obvious that once a species has evolved a strain that can eat such a plant it will probably leave more living offspring than other strains. The next steps, that is the ability to store the toxic substances and carry them over to the adult insect, are additional advantages which may evolve with time. This in turn leads on to warning coloration and the warning way of life.

Poison paradoxes

It should, however, be clearly understood that all Lepidoptera with chemical defence mechanisms do not get their poisons directly from their food plants. Some of these toxic substances are synthesised by the insects themselves. The garden tiger is a good example of this. It is a curious fact that the toxic substance found in its defence glands has only once previously been identified in a living animal; on this occasion it was found in the poison glands of a marine

snail. Furthermore, all insects living on poisonous plants do not store toxins in their bodies. A large number, for example, feed on tobacco and presumably obtain indirect protection by this means, but nicotine is apparently too deadly a poison to store in living tissues and the examples so far examined among tobacco feeders either excrete the poisons rapidly or change them within their bodies into less toxic substances. In such cases the insects concerned are not warningly coloured. However, here again one cannot generalise, for although most insects with poisons in their tissues are brightly coloured, some very toxic nightflying moths have concealing coloration, and almost certainly prove fatal to any unsuspecting animal that consumes them.

Harmless mimic the harmful

Again there are some warningly coloured butterflies which are quite innocuous in reality, but deceitfully resemble (or mimic) those which have chemical defence mechanisms—sheep in wolves' clothing—and thereby gain protection from predators which mistake them for dangerous species. This does not appear to be common among the Lepidoptera of Europe but it is widespread in certain tropical countries. The hornet clearwing of Europe is one example since it looks like a hornet and bears little resemblance to a moth.

The investigation of poisons in insects is rather a difficult matter, since they are present in small quantities and require complicated and time-consuming techniques for their identification. Probably, when more is known about the subject, it will be found that many warningly coloured insects which feed on poisonous plants and can store the toxins in their food have simultaneously evolved the mechanism for secreting additional poisons themselves, or at any rate substances which boost the effect of the main chemical deterrent.

Flight in animals

The natural pioneers of animal flight were the insects. Small, light and charged with energy they took to the air 300 million years ago, some 100 million years before the vertebrates—first the birds and later the bats. Flight was not achieved quickly but only after a long period of trial and error. Flight depends on wings, whose movement through the air produces forces that oppose the downward pull of gravity, and at the same time drive the body forward.

Man had observed flying animals' ability to move through the air for thousands of years, but it was only in this present century that he successfully conquered the air. In Greek mythology, in the first century AD, Lucian prepared Menippus for his first visit to Zeus by equipping him with the right wing of an eagle and the left wing of a vulture. It is interesting to note that Lucian insisted on a series of test flights in accordance with modern practice.

Aerodynamics forefather

The first practical suggestions were put forward by Leonardo da Vinci (1452-1519) but it was 300 years before the foundations of modern aerodynamics were laid down by Sir George Cayley (1773-1851) who applied mechanical principles to the flight mechanisms of birds.

In 1901, two years before his historic flight, Wilbur Wright remarked that a bird's skill as a flyer 'is not apparent . . . we only learn to appreciate it when we try to imitate it'. To become airborne there are many problems, but the overriding consideration is to combine maximum power with minimum weight.

Insects fly more like helicopters than aeroplanes, their oscillating wings providing lift and thrust like the rotors of the helicopter. The frequency of the wingbeats in insects is usually very high; bees average 200 to 300 beats per second and the midges as high as 1 000. Many insects can carry out several manoeuvres—hovering, flying backwards and rising and descending steeply.

Living aeroplanes

Birds of course are the living aeroplanes, each wing functioning efficiently as a combined wing and propeller. The flight of a bird can be divided into flapping flight and gliding flight, birds using these to varying extents.

In flapping flight the pectoral muscles contract, pulling the arm down (see diagram). The resistance of the air to the wing surface produces an upward reaction on the wing. This force is transmitted via the coracoid bones to the sternum, and so acts through the bird's centre of gravity, lifting it as a whole.

Forward momentum is also provided by the slicing action of the wing tip. In the downstroke the leading edge is below the trailing edge so the air is thrust backwards and the bird moves forward. Generally speaking, the primary feathers provide the forward component, and the secondaries provide the lifting force.

The upstroke of the wing is much more rapid than the downstroke. A smaller pectoral muscle when it is contracted raises the wing. Often the arm is simply rotated slightly so the leading edge is higher than the trailing edge and the rush of air lifts the wing. The way in which the primary and secondary feathers overlap produces maximum resistance during the downstroke and minimum in the upstroke.

Thermals and aerofoils

In gliding the wings remain outspread and are used as aerofoils, the bird sliding down a 'cushion' of air, losing height and gaining forward momentum. If a bird glides in air that is rising faster than the bird's forward motion, the bird will soar upwards. In certain hot climate countries, upward currents of warm air alternate with downward currents of cool air, so the birds soar upwards in the former and glide downwards in the latter.

Several gliding animals are dealt with in the encyclopedia. The flying fish and the flying gurnard are examples of animals which develop the necessary motion through the air by their own muscular effort. The flying phalanger, flying lemur, flying squirrel and gliding frog, however, move by falling and gliding under gravity.

The wings, skeleton and the main muscles involved in flight. The huge pectoral muscle makes up as much as ⅕ of the total body weight. When it contracts the wings are depressed. The fibres of this muscle in flying birds are red, due to a copious blood supply, whereas the fibres of birds such as the fowl are white. Elevation of the wing at takeoff is produced by a smaller muscle which lies deep to the pectoral muscle. The joints and muscles of the wing itself serve to spread the wing and to adjust its shape at each beat.

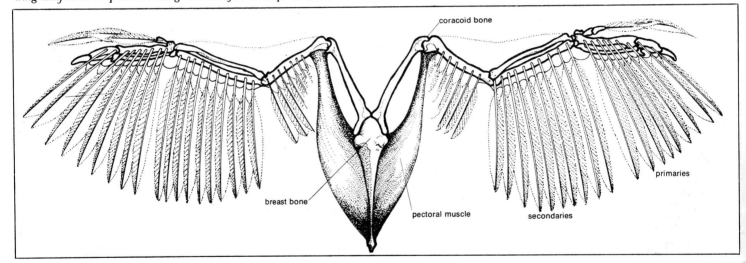

coracoid bone

breast bone

pectoral muscle

secondaries

primaries

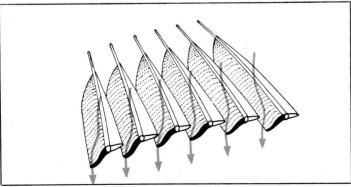

Upstroke: air reaction of the last downstroke forces wing upwards against pressure of the air. The barbs of the primary and secondary feathers allow downward passage, so air flows through with no effort.

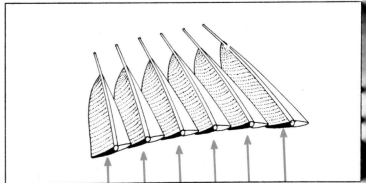

Downstroke: the massive pectoral muscles contract, forcing the pressure to reverse and the barbs to close like the slants of a blind. This stroke imparts lift and propulsion according to the attitude of the bird.

Bluebird ballistics

The eye-baffling details of birds' flight are revealed in this series of pictures of the Canadian bluebird. Each picture required a separate bird flight and was taken at an exposure time of 1/5 000 of a second.

1. Takeoff: as the bluebird leaves its perch the wings are lifted to their highest point. The barbs of the primary feathers open due to the pressure of the air from above. This allows the wings to be raised without much effort, so conserving energy for the next stage.

2. The effective downstroke: this is the power stroke of flight. The barbs of the feathers overlap with the result that a large surface area of wing comes in contact with the air.

3 and 4. Head up, tail down and legs tucked in as the wings move back to add to the streamlined effect and to keep the body level.

5. Coming in to land the legs are lowered and aimed at the perch, while the body rears up and the tail fans out to act as a brake.

6. The feathers pivot to allow air to rush through the wings.

7. Landing: the wings act as balancers and the legs absorb the shock.

Photos by Bernard Corby

The life-span of animals

'Touching on the shortness or length of life in beast, the Knowledge that may be had is slight, the Observation negligent, and the Tradition is fabulous.' That sentence from Francis Bacon's *Historia Vitae et Mortis* (The History of Life and Death) was written in 1623. Today, nearly 350 years later, zoologists attempting to obtain accurate figures relative to the life-span of animals face much the same problems.

Most of our knowledge of the life-span of animals comes from domestic or otherwise captive animals. Domestic animals may have exceptionally long lives but, because of the great differences in environment between them and animals in nature, cannot represent the animal kingdom in general. A captive or domestic animal is fed regularly, is not subjected to drought, flood or bush or forest fire, is not preyed upon by other animals, and when it is injured or falls victim to disease it often receives expert veterinary attention. Consequently it has every chance of a long and healthy life. On the other hand, animals that exist in nature, be they mammals, fish, reptiles or insects, live dangerously and can exist only as long as there is enough suitable food available and they are able to defend themselves against predators. Although ringing or otherwise marking wild animals can give some valuable information on their life-spans, it is by no means conclusive. Indeed, it is very often misleading. Only a few animals that have been marked are found again, so it is not known when their lives ended.

Unlike trees, the age of which can be established with reasonable accuracy from their annular rings, few animals give any visual indication of their age.

Scales reveal age

Many fish reveal their age when caught, from markings on the scales, and a few clams indicate age by lines on the shell. Some tortoises have markings on the shell which are thought to indicate age, but this is still a tentative idea. Similarly, certain North American wild sheep are believed to show their age by the number of segments making up the ram's horns. As the number of segments tends, however, to remain constant after 12 or 14 years, this yardstick is strictly limited.

Among wild game species, the amount of tooth wear and changes in bone structure may yield valuable information about the animal's age, but this is not conclusive.

In general, large animals would appear to live longer than small ones, but there are many exceptions, even within families. On average, the wild lion does not live much longer than its small relative the domestic cat: about 16 years. There are records of zoo lions living for 34 years and of domestic cats reaching 30 years. As a general rule among dogs, the larger the breed, the shorter its life, while among horses the massive shire normally has a shorter life than its little relative the Shetland pony.

Another example of just how unreliable is any attempt to equate size with life-span is provided by comparison between the box turtle and the water turtle. Both these are approximately the same size, but their life-spans differ markedly. There is little difference in size between the spotted salamander and the European salamander, yet the former has much the longer life-span.

Newts which have been marked and then set free in large vivariums where conditions approximate as nearly as possible to those in nature have been known to live for 35 years, whereas seals, hundreds of times bigger than newts, have been marked when pups then liberated to be washed up on beaches 20 years later. Also, according to careful observation, queen bees have been known to

live for up to 7 years, whereas a shrew very rarely lives for longer than 2 years.

Estimates of animal life-spans are particularly unreliable when we come to consider insects. Silverfish have been known to live for 7 years and so outlive the largest of beetles, which seldom live for more than 5 years. Both the common ant and the giant bird-eating spider, many times bigger than the ant, have life-spans of about 18 years.

Elephants' and whales' ages

The danger of accepting size as a measure of animal longevity was strikingly demonstrated in the case of whales and elephants. Because these are the largest of all mammals, responsible zoologists once credited them with life-spans of 150—200 years. Such estimates, arrived at without scientific basis, were effectively demolished by the discovery that the whale has a wax-like plug in its external ear that increases in length with age. The plug also has marks which probably indicate annual growth. Careful examination of the earplugs of hundreds of whales caught in the Antarctic fishing grounds suggests that none was older than 60 years. As for elephants, there is no reliable record of any having lived longer than 77 years.

Large carnivores, and most of the big and medium-sized ungulates, live for about 30 years. Smaller ungulates appear to die of old age at about 25 years, and domestic sheep which have been allowed to live out their lives and die natural deaths have life-spans of approximately 15 years.

Most small birds in the wild have a fairly constant mortality rate regardless of age. Accidents and predators take such heavy toll that few of the small birds live long enough to grow old. Judged from ringing statistics, the life expectancy of wild chaffinches is about 6 months, and any that survive for 3 years are fortunate. Yet wild chaffinches have been kept caged for nearly 30 years—another example of the fallacy of trying to fix animal life-spans from the age of captives.

Birds such as the Arctic tern, ringed to study migration routes, have been found to be still flying when 27 years old. Golden eagles and other large birds of prey have been recorded as living for 80 years, and there are authentic records of pelicans and geese with life-spans of 50 years. Herring gulls have lived for between 40 and 50 years, but the domestic pigeon rarely survives more than 35 years. The life-span of heavy-bodied, non-flying birds seems to

vary inversely with size. The ostrich, with an average life-span of 25 years, lives no longer than many medium-sized birds that have not lost the use of their wings.

Because the age of fish can be estimated from their scales, and fresh-water mussels and anemones are static for much of their existence, the possible life-span of many marine creatures can be judged: and some of them are remarkably long-lived. The sturgeon can claim to be the veteran among fish; specimens have been caught with indications that they were at least 80 years old. Next in seniority are halibut, up to 70 years old, and carp, possibly 50 years old. Sea anemones are known to have lived for 60 years, and lobsters for 50 years.

Probably the longest-lived animals are the tortoises and, with a few exceptions, the greater their size the longer their life-span. This would seem to be due to the fact that they keep growing indefinitely, though the rate of growth diminishes with age. A specimen of the now extinct *Testudo sumeirei* was at least 150 years old when it was accidentally killed in 1919 in the grounds of the military barracks in Mauritius. Its age was attested by army records which from 1768 onwards had mentioned it as a garrison mascot.

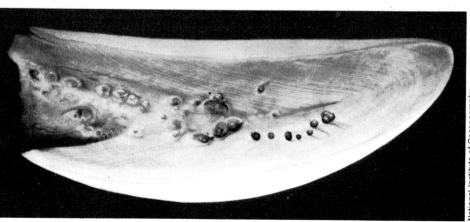

◁ *Polar bear trio—Rack (22 years), Ruin (19 years) living at Chester Zoo, England, can expect to live up to about 34 years of age.*
△ *Close-up of the ear plug from a fin whale in longitudinal section, showing the laminated structure. Each growth layer, of one light and one dark striation, is believed to represent 1 year of age, the most recently formed layers being at the wider end of the 7in.-long plug.*
▷ △ *Tortoises are the symbol of longevity, the South American giant tortoise* Testudo denticulata *is one which lives to a great age.*
▷ *Mandibular tooth of a sperm whale sectioned to show the growth layers in the dentine. Scientists are still not sure whether 1 or 2 years of growth is represented by one growth layer.*

△ *Lar gibbon: average life expectancy 25 years.* △ *A hardy animal of the extreme north, the musk ox can live up to 23 years in the wild.*
▽ *Contrary to early ideas, large size and long life are not always synonymous; the longest recorded life for an elephant is 77 years.*

Insect life histories

Insects belong to the major division or phylum of animals called the Arthropoda, which includes such other groups as the crustaceans, centipedes, millipedes and spiders. One of the characteristics of this phylum is the possession of a jointed external skeleton which serves as a protective skin or shell and also (as our own skeleton does) as an attachment for the muscles. Once it has hardened, however, it cannot stretch, and it does not grow with the animal as our bones do. Consequently the animal can only grow by periodically shedding its outer skin or shell. This shedding or changing of the skin is correctly called *ecdysis*, and the stages between the successive ecdyses are called *instars*. Immediately after ecdysis the new skin, which has developed under the old one, is soft and elastic and there is a short period of rapid growth which ceases as soon as the external covering hardens, and can only be resumed after the next ecdysis.

The life histories of insects, then, consist of a series of stages or instars punctuated by shedding or moulting of the skin, each shedding being called an ecdysis.

An example of the simplest sort of insect life history is that of the silverfish or bristletail, *Lepisma saccharina*. This is a little wingless insect that is found in houses, usually in warm cupboards in the kitchen. It is regarded as primitive, that is to say it resembles the ancestors of all insects, which lived many millions of years ago. From eggs laid by the female tiny silverfishes hatch that differ from their parents only in size. They live and feed just as the adults do, hiding in crevices and eating starchy or sugary substances, and they shed their outer skins repeatedly as they grow, not only the covering of the body but that of the legs and antennae as well. The only change from one instar to the next is of size, and there may be as many as 50 instars in the life of a silverfish. When they reach a certain size they mate and lay eggs, but they continue to renew their outer skins and grow after they have begun breeding.

Now let us look at the life history of a grasshopper, an insect that differs from the silverfish in having wings when it is adult. The insect that hatches from the egg is not unlike a tiny stumpy grasshopper, but it has no wings at all. Five to eight times in the course of growing up it sheds its skin, and after the first or second shedding the wings appear as little pads or flaps. With each successive ecdysis not only does the insect become larger, but the wings become larger relative to its size, until finally they are completely developed and the grasshopper can fly. The fully winged stage is the final instar; after this the grasshopper cannot grow any more. Also it cannot breed until it reaches the final instar, a further point of difference from the silverfish. On the other hand, like the silverfish, the young grasshopper eats the same food and leads an adult sort of life (apart from flying).

In the successive stages of a grasshopper's growth there is a change from a wingless to a winged insect. An animal which changes in form in the course of its growth is said to undergo *metamorphosis*.

Metamorphosis

The third main type of insect life history is well shown by that of a butterfly. Here there emerges from the egg a little worm-like creature totally unlike a butterfly, and we call it a larva or caterpillar. It feeds on leaves and grows rapidly; although the skin of a caterpillar appears soft and flexible it cannot stretch indefinitely and there are several ecdyses in the course of its growth. In preparation the caterpillar spins a mat of silk on a leaf and fastens its rearmost legs to it. Then the skin behind the head splits and the insect crawls out of its old skin, which remains anchored to the silken mat.

When it is fully grown the caterpillar hangs itself up with threads of silk and remains for a day or two without moving. Then another ecdysis takes place, but this time, when the skin is slipped off, a completely different object appears, not a caterpillar at all but a pupa or chrysalis. During the time the larva is hanging up a most extraordinary process takes place. All the muscles and most of the internal organs of the insect have dissolved into a kind of living soup, which then re-forms to build up a butterfly. The chrysalis is really a complete butterfly packed away into a hard capsule; if it is examined carefully the outlines of the legs, wings and antennae of the butterfly can be seen.

After a period of several weeks or months the final ecdysis takes place. The shell of the pupa splits and the butterfly crawls out. At first its wings are like little crumpled bags, but fluid from the body is pumped into them, causing them to expand, and then withdrawn, so that they flatten to form the broad patterned wings of the beautiful perfect insect. The butterfly is now adult; it is ready to breed and it does not grow any more.

Here the metamorphosis that takes place is much more profound than in the case of the grasshopper. The caterpillar crawls about and feeds by chewing up leaves. The butterfly can only suck up liquids through its long coiled proboscis, and feeds mainly on the nectar of flowers. The next-to-last instar, the pupa, or chrysalis, has no external limbs or mouth-parts and cannot move about or feed at all.

The kind of metamorphosis they undergo is an important point in the classification of insects: the life of the grasshopper gives an example of *incomplete metamorphosis*, that of the butterfly of *complete metamorphosis*. Only a few primitive kinds of insects develop, like the silverfish, without any metamorphosis.

Other groups in which it is incomplete

▷△△ *Simple insect life history — silverfish. The young are exact replicas of their parents, and grow simply by shedding their skins. They may do this up to 50 times during their lives.*
▷△ *The incomplete metamorphosis of the grasshopper. The young resemble the adult but are wingless. Wing buds appear after the first one or two moults of the skin.*
▷ *Complete metamorphosis — the butterfly. Here there are two completely different intermediate stages: the active, feeding caterpillar and the inert but developing chrysalis.*

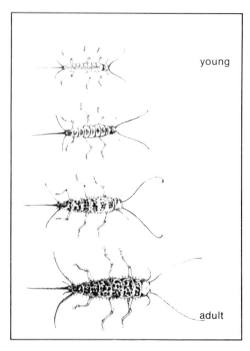

young

adult

eggs

wings absent

wing buds formed

adult or imago

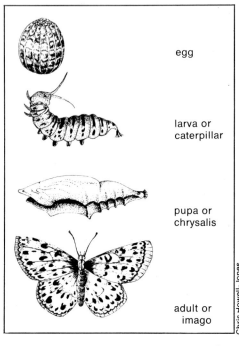

egg

larva or caterpillar

pupa or chrysalis

adult or imago

are the true bugs, the cockroaches, the dragonflies and the mayflies. Ants, bees and wasps, beetles and flies have complete metamorphoses like that of butterflies and moths.

Dragonflies and mayflies pass all the instars previous to the winged stage in water. In almost all insects there is no further ecdysis after the wings are developed, but the dragonflies and mayflies form a unique exception to this rule. When it is fully grown but still wingless the insect crawls out of the water, its skin splits and a winged 'fly' emerges and flies a little way. It then settles and another ecdysis takes place producing the final winged stage.

The time that insects take to complete their growth varies widely and is generally less in warmer climates. In the tropics butterflies and moths complete their growths only 3 or 4 weeks after hatching from the egg, while in temperate regions many of them take a year and appear on the wing regularly at a certain season. In northern regions, near the Arctic Circle, many of the larger species take 2 years to complete their growth. The North American periodical cicada passes its early stages underground and takes the astonishing period of 17 years to come to maturity.

Having crawled wingless from the water, moulted to a winged form and flown to a twig, an adult dragonfly emerges after its final moult.

The metamorphosis of insects

The transformation of the caterpillar into the butterfly or of the grub into the bee has always been an object of wonder. The classic explanation, put forward by Aristotle, was that the insect larva is a 'walking egg'. That is, it is an embryo which has left the egg at an early stage of its development. But the larva is not an embryo; it is a highly

stretch to some extent but it cannot grow; and in the harder parts, as in the head of a caterpillar, it cannot even stretch. At intervals, therefore, a new and larger cuticle is formed; and then the old cuticle is shed or thrown off (moulted). It is during the time just before the new cuticle is laid down that true growth, that is, the multiplication of the epidermal cells, takes place. Once the epidermal cells begin to form the new cuticle, their growth and

development. They do not take part in laying down the cuticle of the larva but form clusters of embryonic cells which are destined to grow into the wings, legs etc. of the pupa and subsequently of the adult insect. These clusters of cells (called 'imaginal buds'—the adult insect being called the 'imago') were at one time thought to be characteristic of metamorphosis. Metamorphosis was described as being the result of a renewal of 'imaginal bud' growth.

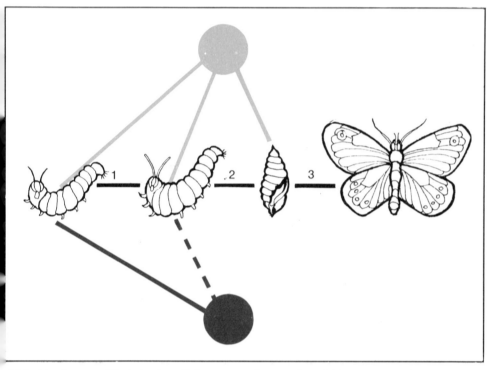

1 Moulting hormone (blue) plus juvenile hormone (red) acts on larval skin to cause moult into another larva. 2 Moulting hormone plus a small amount of juvenile hormone causes moult into pupa. 3 Moulting hormone alone acts on pupal skin to cause moult into adult.

*Celebrated laboratory animal: the South American bloodsucking bug **Rhodnius**, the subject of most insect hormone experiments.*

organized creature closely adapted to the special conditions of its life. The explanation that is accepted today was due to Charles Darwin, who pointed out that when the young insect and the adult insect began to feed on different foods in different surroundings they began to evolve separately in progressive adaptation to their distinctive modes of life; and that when the larva and adult became widely different, a third, intermediate stage, the chrysalis or pupa was evolved to bridge the structural gap.

This interpretation left unsolved the mystery of how the capacity to build the two (or three) forms of the body is stored in the egg. It is now realized that this capacity is stored in the so-called 'genetic code', which contains instructions for the development of the organism. The insect has three sets of instructions, for larva, pupa and adult, and these are brought into operation in succession in every individual. The switch over from one programme of instructions to the next is brought about by hormones discharged into the blood by glands comparable with the pituitary gland or the thyroid gland of mammals.

Growing in spurts

The entire body of the insect is covered by a non-living skin or shell, called a 'cuticle' which is laid down by a single sheet of epidermal cells. In the softer parts, as in the body of a caterpillar, the cuticle can

multiplication necessarily ceases.

Thus growth in the insect takes place in a succession of spurts, each ended by a moult. This whole process is set in train by the 'moulting hormone'. This consists of two components: (i) an *activation hormone* that is secreted by special 'neurosecretory' cells in the brain and set free into the blood. This brain hormone acts upon a gland of internal secretion that usually lies in the thorax (the 'prothoracic gland') and causes this to liberate (ii) the true moulting hormone named *ecdysone* (ecdysis=moulting). This moulting hormone acts directly on those parts of the body concerned in growth, particularly the epidermis, and starts the whole process of cell multiplication.

The moulting process is the basis of metamorphosis. It is only at the time of moulting that change in form can take place. And since it is not possible to see the growth processes that are going forward under the cuticle, any change in form that may occur becomes visible only when the old cuticle is shed. It therefore appears to have taken place abruptly. In some (hemimetabolous) insects, such as the cockroach, the cells that multiply and grow outwards to form the wings, for example, are derived from the rudimentary wings of the larva; in other (holometabolous) insects, such as the butterfly, in which a more extreme type of metamorphosis takes place, certain epidermal cells are set aside at an early stage of

Repressed adults

One might have expected that metamorphosis, that is, the setting in train of all the growth processes required to carry out the programme of instructions that will lead to the pupal form and then the adult form, would be brought about by a 'metamorphosis hormone'. But such a hormone has never been found. Metamorphosis is controlled in the opposite way: all larval stages contain an 'anti-metamorphosis hormone', which ensures that the larval programme of growth is maintained.

The juvenile hormone is secreted by a small gland of internal secretion, termed the corpus allatum, which lies just behind the brain. Throughout the larval stages the corpus allatum keeps up the secretion of the juvenile hormone, and when moulting occurs the larval form is maintained. But when the larva is full-grown the corpus allatum (controlled by the brain) no longer secretes the juvenile hormone. When growth and moulting take place under the action of the moulting hormone, in the presence of a very small amount of juvenile hormone, the pupal programme of growth is brought into action. On the other hand, when the juvenile hormone is absent altogether, the adult programme comes into operation and the final step in metamorphosis occurs. Both ecdysone and the juvenile hormone have been isolated and their chemical composition is known.

Organs of special sense

An animal's sense organs are its information receivers, its contact with the outside world. To do the right things at the right time an animal must be aware of its surroundings. Animals do not receive stimuli in the same way that we do; their sense organs are adapted to their own way of life. This is particularly reflected in their eyes. An animal's behaviour patterns and its eye position and pupil shape are very closely correlated. It is even possible for an animal to have three eyelids, the third eyelid or nictitating membrane being yet another specific adaptation to the animal's environment. The king vulture's third eyelid, for example, acts as a windproofing goggle.

The sense organs by which insects receive light stimuli show even more complexity and adapatation to their behavioural patterns. Insect eyes are of two types: simple and compound. Unlike other animals' eyes they cannot be closed. Their vision is sharp for only a few feet, but the compound eyes are extremely good at detecting movement. This is of prime importance for insects, as a moving object either means prey or, more probably, a predator. Insects live in a world of colour but they do not perceive the same range of colours that we do. Bees for instance can 'see' ultra-violet light, a wavelength that is invisible to us. This wavelength perception is important especially to flowers for their pollination. Insects also use their eyes to navigate in relation to the sun and moon.

Organs of sense peculiar to certain fish are electric organs. Why some fish have the ability to generate electricity is not really understood. The obvious functions are to stun prey, defence and a means of helping a fish live and detect prey in murky waters.

The skin responds both to external and internal stimuli and is vital to a mammal's wellbeing; it regulates temperature, protects and is extremely sensitive to environmental changes. Skin is present as hooves, claws and nails as well as a body-enveloping membrane.

Animal eyes and their ways of life

Animals' eyes are so well adapted to their ways of life that they tell much about the animals themselves. We can learn from eyes where creatures live, when and what they eat, and how much they depend on sight.

Eyelids became essential when animals with their aquatic eyes left the drying pools of Devonian times. Eyes that were once cradled in water, safe from drying, abrasion and glare became protected in individual 'eyecups', holding soothing tears. Today, we see how added structures in these eyelids cope with a variety of habitats.

To an Egyptian skink, for example, wind-driven desert sand is no problem — the lizard can close its eyes and see through clear windows in its lower lids.

Again, a Cuban toad, *Empusus*, has extra-wide upper eyelids which fold down over the raised lower lids like envelope flaps to seal the eyes against dirt in the burrow.

The third eyelid

Most useful in nature are the third sets of eyelids (nictitating membranes) which are extremely helpful for creatures which cannot otherwise wipe their eyes — they have, in fact, been called nature's handkerchiefs. As these lids fan over the eyeballs in side-wise winks, they spread lubrication; as they snap back they comb under the upper and lower lids and sweep the eyeball to remove chance debris. These third eyelids vary greatly. Among them, transparent ones form waterproofing goggles for penguins and other birds that speed through the water, or windproofing goggles for birds that rush through the air in pursuit of prey. For the ground-feeding birds, translucent lids are the rule; the shoebill stork's third eyelids are opaque, giving the impression of being most protective.

Other classes of animals have a variety of third eyelids. One big mammal, a llama, has third lids supported by a T-shaped cartilage. To remove chaff from its eye, the beast extends the third lid, then rolls its eye towards the stiff edge of it, as we would scrape a boot on a foot scraper.

We can find how much an animal depends on sight by the relative size of its eyes. A

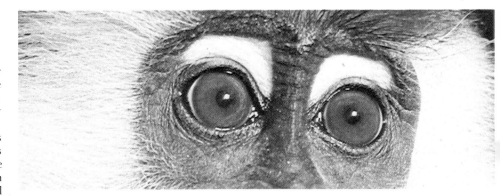

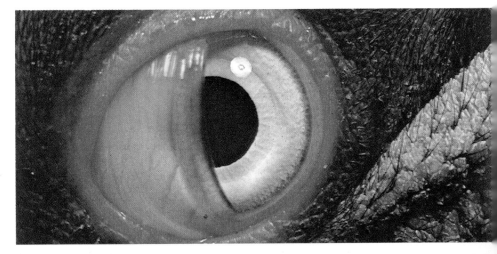

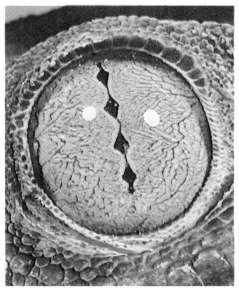

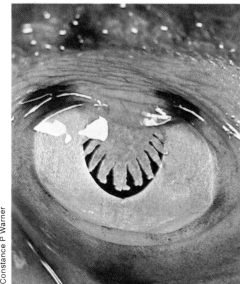

Constance P Warner

mole rat's eyes are very small – it needs only to sense its nearness to light and possible capture. On the other hand a nocturnal flying squirrel has relatively enormous eyes, to gather as much moonlight as possible to judge jumps in the trees.

Position of eyes

Eyes close together give an owl overlapping vision from the two sides for accurate distance judgement when pouncing on prey; eyes widely separated give a prairie dog a view of the whole terrain to help it avoid predators. Eyes on top of the head allow a clawed frog to see food as it filters down through the pond above.

The pupils, too, are highly versatile. These iris openings not only extend in special directions to increase a subject's visual field but by extreme contractions they achieve the advantages of pinhole cameras.

One of the few snakes with sharp sight, a vine snake, has pupils shaped like keyholes. Through the handle of the keyhole this snake sees all movements to the side; along the long end of the key it gets good vision forward, so it can remain motionless until the moment it strikes at passing prey.

For the creatures we usually see feeding by day, round pupils which contract and expand to regulate the light reaching the retinas, serve their purpose well; but for animals whose eyes are built for dim light, daylight is always too bright: single contracting round pupils do not suffice. Hence the odd shapes of some pupils.

Penguin's pupils

Perhaps the most active pupils are those of penguins. As they hunt in the dimness of the ocean, their pupils are large in an effort to get light enough to focus on passing fish. But when penguins vault from the sea onto the glaring ice their pupils contract through an astonishingly fast series of round, star-shaped and square forms until they become the tiniest of squares.

Tropical geckos not only scamper over walls, feeding at night but are active by day. When light comes, their big scallop-edged irises come together and overlap, leaving four pinholes as pupils in between. These pinhole apertures not only pass four sharp images that focus as one on the retinas but the eyes are relieved of undue light.

For another dim light dweller, the skate, which lives at the sea bottom but comes to the surface at times, little finger-like processes form at the top of the pupil when the light is bright, to shade the eyes.

These few examples of the many animals' eyes show that each is elegantly adapted to its environment and way of life.

Opposite page. Top: Primate's large, forward-directed eyes have full stereoscopic vision.
Centre: The third eyelid fans over a king vulture's eye to clean and windproof.
Bottom left: A gecko's eye is relieved of too much light by the scallop-edged pupils.
Bottom right: Finger-like processes shade the skate's eye when it comes to the surface.
This page. Top: rows of 100 or more beady eyes gleam amongst the scallop's tentacles.
Bottom: prominent eyes of a puffer. Eyes on the side of the head give fishes monocular vision.

Jane Burton: Photo Res

Jane Burton: Photo Res

The eyes of insects

Insect eyes are of two basic types—simple and compound. They are rigidly fixed in the insect's head and can neither move nor focus on near and distant objects. Simple eyes, or ocelli, are the only visual organs present in insect larvae and arachnids, whereas adult insects and the nymphs of those insect orders which undergo only partial metamorphosis often have both compound and simple eyes. In passing it is interesting to note that mealworms and some other beetle larvae respond to light even after their eyes have been covered, due to a general light-sensitivity of their skin.

The simple eye
A simple eye consists of a crude lens formed by an outwardly domed, transparent patch of cuticle, behind which lies a group of light-sensitive cells forming a simple retina which is linked by nerve fibres to the creature's brain. The lens is part of the insect's skin and is shed at each moult and grown anew.

Ocelli show considerable variation in their anatomy and visual ability, but probably reach their greatest development in the jumping spiders and the larvae of tiger beetles. The former can accurately locate its prey from up to 3 in. Even in the case of the most highly developed simple eyes however, it is doubtful whether much more than a vague image is received due to the limitation of the lens, and the relatively few sense cells in the retina.

If we examine a caterpillar's head through a hand lens its simple eyes will be seen as a semi-circle of (usually six) minute black dots which lie just above and to either side of its mouth. The retina of these simple eyes is formed into a rod, one end of which faces the light. Between the lens and this retinal rod lies a cone of crystalline material which serves to concentrate the light leaving the lens onto the end of this rod. This is unlike the more advanced simple eyes in which the retina, like our own, is laid down carpet fashion behind the lens.

Because the retinal rod behaves as a single light perceiving element an eye of this construction cannot register a pattern, but merely a single point of light corresponding to the average brightness of the scene within its narrow field of view. As it is equipped, however, with several of these eyes, each facing in a slightly different direction, by scanning its head from side to side a larva can build up quite an adequate picture of its surroundings.

The compound eye
The remarkable organs known as compound eyes are found only in insects and crustaceans, and always occur as a pair. These elaborate structures comprise a large number of individual eye units known as ommatidia, whose basic construction is similar to that of the simple eyes of the caterpillar. Because they are longer and thinner than simple eyes, many ommatidia may be packed side by side across the surface of a compound eye. They are cone shaped, and usually have hexagonal lenses, which give the surface of a compound eye the appearance of a microscopic honeycomb. The typical diameter of one of these facets is about thirty thousandths of a millimetre, $\frac{1}{780\,000}$ in.

Each ommatidium sees only a very small

Battery of eyes: this formidably beady stare comes from a wolf spider—a relation of the insects—which has eight simple eyes, four above, in two pairs, and four below, in a line. Despite their number these impressive eyes give only a vague outline of the spider's prey.

segment of the scene, perceiving it as one point of light of a particular intensity which is transmitted as a corresponding nerve signal to the insect's brain. Here the nerve impulses from all the ommatidia are combined to create an impression of the original scene. It will be appreciated that the greater the number of ommatidia making up a compound eye the finer will be the mosaic of light dots seen, and hence the better resolution of fine detail. Certain ants have only six ommatidia per eye, the housefly has 4 000, and dragonflies, so adept at catching minute prey in flight, have up to 28 000. But when these figures are compared with those for the human eye which carries some 100 million visual elements it will be realised that insect vision must be very indistinct.

Experiments have shown that many insects have well-developed colour vision that is somewhat different from our own. Their eyes are sensitive to the blue end of the spectrum and to many insects the colour that we see as red appears black, while ultra-violet, invisible to us, is seen by them as a distinct colour.

Because they reflect ultra-violet light, flowers that appear a particular colour to our eyes will be seen by a foraging honeybee quite differently. Many flowers that we consider rather dull appear vividly colourful to an insect, and some blooms have special ultra-violet reflecting areas surrounding the entrance to their nectaries. Invisible to us, these appear as conspicuous bull's eyes to the bee.

Navigating eyes

Compound eyes are remarkably efficient instruments of navigation. An insect is able to move in a straight line by using the sun or moon as a reference point and travelling in such a way that light strikes its eye at a constant angle, so that its image stays within the field of view of a selected group of ommatidia. The moth that ends up in the candle flame only does so because it inadvertently chose this local light source as a reference instead of the distant moon. The moth soon finds itself flying past the candle and has to turn inwards in order to maintain the same angle between itself and the light. As it continues to fly the moth must turn constantly inwards, pursuing a diminishing spiral path towards the flame.

By means of the retinal cells in their ommatidia many insects can detect the polarisation (plane of vibration) of light from the sky and they use this ability to orientate themselves accurately. Skylight polarisation varies according to the direction of the sky area from which it comes, and the height of the sun. It is not difficult to understand that an insect can associate a particular pattern of light polarisation with a given compass direction, but just how the effect of the sun's changing height is taken into account is another of nature's unsolved mysteries.

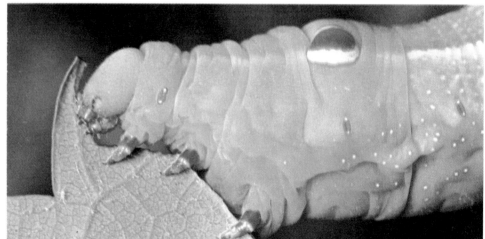

△ △ ▷ *Out on stalks: the compound eyes of diopsid flies are at the end of rigid stalks.*
△ ▷ *The hawk moth caterpillar's big eye spot is a body marking; 2 pairs of tiny true simple eyes are found on the head.*
▷ *The large, bean-like compound eye of the grasshopper has a small simple eye next to it.*

Electric organs in fishes

Electrogenic organs are found in both marine and freshwater members of the bony fishes and the cartilaginous fishes (rays). The functions of the organs include stunning the prey, defence, as well as helping the fish to find its way about and locate its food in muddy waters.

The benefit of such an unusual organ to the fish is not always obvious to us, and the situation may be further complicated by the fish using its powers of electrical discharge in more than one way.

In the stargazers, *Astroscopus* species (which are the only electric bony fishes living in salt water), the electric organs, which can generate about 50 volts, are located in deep pits behind the eyes. The way in which the stargazers use these organs is not known for certain, but it is most likely for defence or feeding. Unlike the electric ray the ventral surface of the stargazer is the positive side.

The thornback ray *Raia clavata* and some of its relatives, have weak electric organs in the tail which can generate about 4 volts. It is apparently difficult to persuade the fish to discharge its electricity, and its purpose is unknown, although Dr ME Brown has suggested that low voltage discharges may provide some means for species or sex recognition.

The electric eel uses its organs both for stunning its prey and for finding its way about. The electric catfish and the electric rays *(Narcine, Torpedo)* use their electricity for both defence and feeding.

Gymnarchus, a fish from the Nile, and the related African mormyrid fishes use their organs to surround themselves with an electric field (rather like that around a magnet) in which any disturbances caused by nearby objects can be detected by receptors in the skin; this enables the mormyrids (elephant snout fishes) to find their way about in muddy waters, and *Gymnarchus* to navigate into crevices in the rocks or when the visibility is poor.

Structure and physiology

Every time a muscle is contracted in your body a tiny electric impulse is involved in the transmission of the command from the nerve to the muscle. In all the electric fishes, muscles have become modified in such a way that their contractile powers have been abolished whilst their electrical properties have been enhanced.

In one of the rays, Dr Ewart found that in the young the muscle fibres were normal, but as the fish grew, the anterior ends of the fibres ballooned out and the nerve endings became concentrated there whilst the posterior ends of the fibres became reduced. One such unit is an electroplate. In *Astroscopus* and some others several muscle fibres fuse to form the electroplate, but the nerves always become concentrated at one end of the modified fibre instead of spreading all over it.

In an adult fish each electric organ is built up from a large number of electroplates, most of them facing the same way in the same species. Each electroplate is surrounded by a jelly-like substance and contained in a box of connective tissue. The jelly contains the fine blood capillaries which keep the electroplate provided with nutrients. The electroplates in the electric eel can produce a potential of 150mV each, and the nerve endings (the motor end plates) are on the negative side of the unit. The spacing and number of the electroplates within the organ varies with the species of fish. It is the transparent jelly and the clear cytoplasm of the cells that make the organs look so transparent and conspicuous in the adult.

Most of the electroplates in *Electrophorus* are arranged in series to give a large voltage to overcome the high electrical resistance of fresh water but a few units are arranged in parallel to produce a high amperage pulse of short duration which is used for direction finding.

The discharge of the organs is controlled by nerves which may arise from prominent electric lobes in the brain (in *Torpedo* and *Narcine*) or from the spinal cord in the electric eel and mormyrids. In the electric catfish the organs sheath much of the body and are formed from muscle in the same way as in the other electric fishes, not from glandular tissue as was long thought.

The production and release of electricity within the organs appears to be similar to that in our own muscles in which a chemical called acetylcholine (ACh) is released at the end plate of the nerve by the impulse passing down the nerve from the brain. ACh causes various electrically charged particles (ions) to move and change places and this is the source of the electricity. As the end plates are much more concentrated, and are arranged differently in these organs, so the electrical output is much greater than in our own muscles.

The large stunning shocks are the result of the almost simultaneous discharge of all the electroplates whilst the regular small pulses represent a discharge from a few electroplates (usually in parallel) under direct control of the nerve.

It was a puzzle for a long time why electric fishes did not shock themselves. One of the answers to this lies in the fact that the nerves, especially in the electric eel, are very heavily insulated. Even so, much more research is needed.

The independent development of electric organs in several totally unrelated groups of fishes is a most interesting example of convergence, various aspects of which fascinated Charles Darwin.

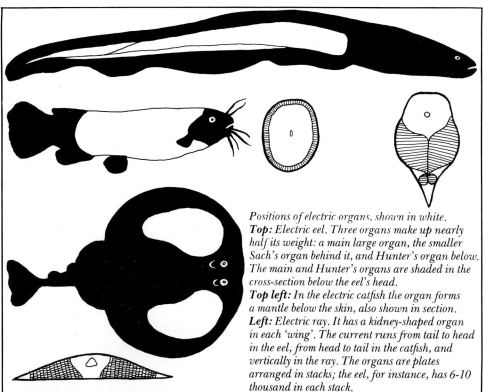

Positions of electric organs, shown in white.
Top: *Electric eel. Three organs make up nearly half its weight: a main large organ, the smaller Sach's organ behind it, and Hunter's organ below. The main and Hunter's organs are shaded in the cross-section below the eel's head.*
Top left: *In the electric catfish the organ forms a mantle below the skin, also shown in section.*
Left: *Electric ray. It has a kidney-shaped organ in each 'wing'. The current runs from tail to head in the eel, from head to tail in the catfish, and vertically in the ray. The organs are plates arranged in stacks; the eel, for instance, has 6-10 thousand in each stack.*

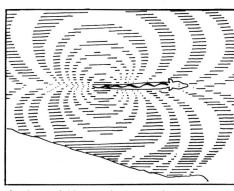

△ *Electric field around* **Gymnarchus**.
▽ *Diagrammatic arrangement of electric organs — a living battery with plates in series.*

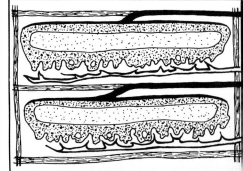

The skin as a versatile organ

The body of a mammal is an intricate living machine, whose proper working and survival depends upon its prompt response to an immense variety of both external and internal changes. For successful activity its several parts, organs and body-systems, must achieve the highest degree of co-ordination and in this the skin plays a vital role. Primarily the impervious exterior wrapping or rind of the body, it interposes between the internal and external environments and responds to stimuli from both. Its functions are therefore many, diverse and very important, and are associated with those of the nervous system, the hormones, the temperature regulating mechanism and the water elimination apparatus.

The skin has two layers: the deeper (dermis, cutis vera) is a dense, tough felt-work of connective and elastic tissue, impervious to fluids and becoming leather on tanning; the outer (epidermis, scarf skin) is an avascular varnish of flat cells, disposed in layers, continuously renewed and readily worn away. Out-growths of the epidermis include hairs (peculiar to the class Mammalia) nails, claws, hooves, and a variety of glands, implanted in the dermis. Sebaceous glands are isolated tubes which lose heat and water from the body as sweat; modified sebaceous glands include the mammary glands (another mammalian characteristic) and a host of scent glands of diverse function.

Protection

In its basic protective capacity the skin prevents the merely mechanical loss of water from the body tissues. Conversely it protects these soft parts against direct damage, whether mechanical, thermal, chemical or bacteriological. The normal skin withstands contact with degrees of hardness and roughness, of heat and cold, of acid and alkali, intolerable to the deeper tissues, whilst by keeping out micro-organisms that could lead to disease it is a natural antiseptic.

Sensation

Throughout life sensory information reaches the mammal's body continuously. Some is long-distance information from remote objects, sensed by the olfactory epithelium of the nose, the retina of the eye, and the Corti organ of the ear. Short-distance information is conveyed by stimuli from the immediate external environment, touching the skin. This information must be appreciated by suitable receptor organs and transmitted immediately to the conscious levels of the nervous system, to be there integrated with sensory information from other sources, so that prompt and appropriate response may be made. This skin therefore becomes a sensorium, able to appreciate and transmit to the brain the impressions of touch, pressure, pain, roughness, smoothness, heat, cold, hardness, softness and the simultaneous contact of many objects. To do this it has many highly specialised receptor organs in the dermis upon the ends of the sensory nerves to the skin. Along these nerves and the spinal cord sensory

Hairs for defence: predator's view of the porcupine's modified hair — its sharp spines.

information from the skin reaches the highest functional levels of the brain. Thus skin and brain are most intimately associated, which is not surprising as they have a common embryonic origin. Naturally, those skin areas in most direct contact with the external environment are the most sensitive — the palms, soles, buttocks, and in quadrupeds such as mammals, the face. The skin of the questing quadruped head often has a series of special tactile hairs (vibrissae or 'whiskers') attended at their roots by elaborate sensory nerve endings, which, when these hairs are stimulated, trigger directly to the brain the information thus received.

Temperature regulation

Vital to the mammal's wellbeing is the maintenance of normal body temperature, a function controlled by the brain. In this maintenance the skin plays its part, since according to body activity or environmental requirement the heat may need to be conserved or eliminated.

The skin helps conserve body heat by providing non-conducting material at the body surface, either as hair coat or an underlying layer of insulating fat — hence

Cross-section of skin of a dog's back, showing the hairs, each with its own erecting muscle.

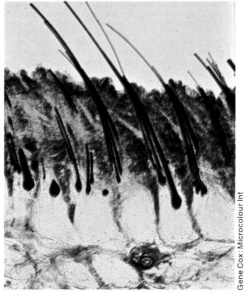

in many mammals the coat of short or long hair, of fur or even wool, but in non-hairy forms (man, pig, whale) the development of a subcutaneous layer of fat. The typical mammalian hair coat has an undercoat of short, soft, vellus hairs and a greater or lesser admixture of longer, coarser hairs. These last are removed in converting a natural pelt into the 'skin' of commerce. In man, but not in apes and monkeys, the long coarse hairs are peculiarly restricted to scalp, beard area, armpits and pubes.

The skin helps eliminate heat (in the form of warm fluid) by means of sweat glands, varying much in number and distribution, and sometimes specially modified to effect a copious and instantaneous discharge of fluid. The extent of heat loss by sweating is at any time conditioned by such factors as muscular activity, external temperature and state of health.

Equally important for the mammalian internal milieu is a controlled removal of water from the body. This is effected by the joint operation of the kidneys, lungs and skin. When exterior cold prevails, most water is eliminated as urine and as water vapour in the air expired: when exterior warmth predominates, most is eliminated in the form of sweat. Thus the skin plays an essential role in maintaining the constancy of the body's internal environment by providing part of the machinery necessary to a controlled elimination of both body heat and body fluid.

Secretion

All subprimate mammals are dominated behaviourally by olfaction: they may be said to 'live' through the nose. By smell they recognise their fellows, their offspring, the opposite sex and their food. Not surprisingly, therefore, sweat glands are developed in great variety of form and situation in the skin of most subprimates. The odorous secretion of these glands marks the animal's trail, or resting place, its den or hide, the trysting place of the sexes and the confines of its territory. The scent produced, whether windborne or trail-laid, gives information to predators hunting for food. Dominant among specialised sebaceous glands is the mammary gland, distinguishing mammals from all other vertebrate classes, and present in all forms, including even the lowly egg-laying monotremes. Upon its secretion (milk) the newborn mammal depends in its early life.

Mammal skin may develop certain distinctive defence structures. Thus particular scent glands may discharge an obnoxious secretion (skunk, polecat), hairs may be modified into sharp-pointed spines (echidna, porcupine, hedgehog), an encasing armour of scales may be developed (pangolin, armadillo) or a special type of horn may be formed (rhinoceros).

Thus, though basically the impermeable body envelope, the mammal skin is much more. Its secondary but equally vital functions transform it into an extremely complex, sensitive, vascular and adaptable organ, essential to the harmony of the internal environment and facilitating appropriate and prompt response to the ever changing demands of the external environment upon the individual mammal.

Behaviour

The study of behaviour is still in its early stages of development. Not a study that depends on elaborate apparatus, but one of patient observation, it has so many aspects that have yet to be explored that it is impossible to give clear-cut reasons for an animal's actions.

A quick and rough definition of behaviour can be that it is simply the movements that animals make. Movement in this sense is not just locomotion, such as running, swimming and crawling, but also feeding, mating and even breeding. Even the slight movements made by animals, such as pricking the ears, are parts of behaviour. All the movements of an animal are remarkably efficient. This is achieved through co-ordination by the central nervous system, which receives stimuli from the sense organs. The function and significance of some of the sense organs has been delt with in the previous chapter. Behaviour is also controlled internally by hormones—chemical messengers—that provide stimuli. Reproductive behaviour is a good example of this.

Behaviour patterns fall into two categories: those that are inbred like any other physical attribute and those that are acquired. Instinctive behaviour and trial and error learning are considered in the discussion on monkey behaviour. It is un-nerving to discover that we can learn a lot about our own behavioural patterns from the study of other primates. The intricate and ritualised flight patterns of butterfly courtship provide an example of inbred behaviour.

An essential part of an animal's equipment for survival, behavioural patterns must be adaptable and able to fit in with environmental changes. This is exemplified in the case of dogs, very successful carnivores; the members of the family Canidae, wild dogs, wolves and foxes, have a practically worldwide distribution.

Monkey manners

There are two basic types of animal behaviour: instinctive and trial and error learning. In addition the higher animals especially show to a varying degree a mental quality which almost defies definition. We call it intelligence. The first, the instinctive, is a built-in, almost machine-like sort of behaviour. When an animal's sense-organs—its eyes, ears, or nostrils—receive a certain signal, the right action is produced automatically. For example, if an enemy comes too close most animals will instinctively try to get away without pausing to work out that this is the best thing to do.

Almost all animal behaviour is instinctive but a few species also show a fair degree of intelligent behaviour. This can be compared with the action of a computer, a very complicated machine which can store a great deal of information in its memory and, when the need arises, sort through it to produce the answers to very tricky problems. Intelligent behaviour also depends upon stored facts, and therefore upon learning, but it enables animals which possess it to solve much more difficult problems.

Mammals show more intelligence than any other class of animals, though many of them do not show very much of it. The most intelligent mammals are in the primates, the group which contains not only man, the most intelligent animal which has ever lived on earth, but also the apes, monkeys, and their relations. The more primitive of these, such as the aye-aye and the bushbabies of Africa, are probably no more intelligent than many other mammals, such as squirrels. They manage to live successful lives largely by instinct, waking up in the evening in response to the fading daylight, moving about in their own familiar territory in search of food, and so on. Because they are more intelligent, monkeys such as the baboon have more varied behaviour than this, and the larger apes—chimpanzee, orang-utan and gorilla—which are very intelligent have very varied behaviour.

Brainy chimpanzees

Much that we know about intelligence results from studying the behaviour of chimpanzees. Whilst they are playing, young

Zool Soc London

△ *Primate puzzles: opening a safe and other complex problems can be solved by simple reasoning.*
▽ *Collective combing: Old World sacred baboons groom each other's fur as a sign of affection.*

chimps learn about the world around them and unconsciously store away facts which may come in useful later. For example, if they have the chance to play with sticks they will learn that a stick can be used to help them reach farther. This information may not be used for a long time, but is stored in the brain until needed.

Later if the chimpanzee is shown some food beyond the bars of its cage which it cannot reach, it will immediately use a stick

to drag the food towards it. Similarly, chimpanzees which are allowed to play with large boxes soon learn that by standing on a box they become taller. Later they can put this knowledge to good use, and will even pile up several boxes to make a platform from which they can reach food hung high above their heads. You can sometimes see chimpanzees performing tricks like this at a zoo. Orang-utans are rarer, and have not been studied as much as

Shy baby orang clings to mother, who aided the delivery and breathed into baby's mouth without previously having seen a young of her own kind.

chimpanzees, but they probably are just as intelligent although they are less excitable and usually move more slowly. The intelligence of gorillas has hardly been studied at all. This is because only recently have young gorillas been successfully kept in captivity. Studies of this kind can be made on young animals only, for most adult primates are bad-tempered, and often savage. Gorillas, however, are probably at least as intelligent as chimpanzees. They should be, for they have larger brains, although the brain of a gorilla is only half the size of a man's.

Instinct to the fore

Although the great apes are so intelligent a great deal of their behaviour is still instinctive. For example, they live in groups not because they have worked out intelligently that this is the best thing for them to do, but because instinctively they are attracted towards others of their own kind. Animals which behave in this way are said to have strong social instincts. Monkeys are also social animals and usually live in quite large troops. Within each troop every monkey knows its own place. To some of its neighbours it must show respect, for they will have proved, either by bluff or by fighting, that they are the fiercer and stronger, whilst it can treat others with much less ceremony. This means that a simple language is necessary, and because monkeys have good hearing and eyesight their language consists largely of making noises and pulling faces. If two Old World monkeys are friendly towards each other, when they meet each will rapidly and repeatedly smack its lips together. This is a friendly signal, and can be compared with the human smile. Often the two friends will then prove their fondness for each other by grooming each other's fur. If a monkey meets another of which it is rather shy it makes a different signal. This consists of a rapid series of grunts, made with the mouth open. It means: 'Although you and I are both very fierce-looking, we won't hurt each other, will we?'

You can sometimes see zoo monkeys making these signals. If you are prepared to let other people think you are a little odd you might even try talking in monkey language to zoo monkeys yourself. Quite often they will answer you. It may seem strange that monkeys should be willing to talk their own language to human beings, but after all pet dogs talk to us in their own language. Tail-wagging is not exactly a human way of signalling!

The behaviour of the other primates teaches us a lot about our own behaviour. Although we are extremely intelligent we still have plenty of instincts, and the two kinds of behaviour are mixed up in almost everything that we do. We are social animals, and soon learn to whom we must be polite and to whom we need not. We have a territory within which we usually stay, although more than other animals we sometimes leave it. However, our territory means a great deal to us. It is no accident that football teams are most likely to win on their own home grounds. We show our intelligence by learning to speak difficult languages whilst we are still quite young, but even whilst we are speaking we still make instinctive signals like smiling or frowning. We are more intelligent than our closest non-human relations, but the difference is much smaller than we often like to think.

Behaviour in dogs

Wild dogs, wolves, and foxes (the Canidae) are probably the most successful of the carnivores because they can and do adapt to many different environmental conditions, including man's destruction of their natural habitat. Take the example of the coyote. During the past 50 years, the face of North America has altered radically through in-dustrialisation and yet the coyote, which has been continuously persecuted by man, has actually increased its range and can now be found in several parts of the United States where it had not been observed before. And the English red fox, an animal which should feed mainly on rabbits and small rodents, now ravages dustbins and eats a large quan-tity of fruit since the 1956 outbreak of myxomatosis produced a sharp decrease in the number of rabbits. This ability to change with the external conditions is a special feature of the Canidae and explains their wide distribution in every continent except Antarctica and in habitats as diverse as the North African deserts, the Arctic tundra, and the South American tropical forests.

Although the species are variable in their size and the colour of their fur, all of the dogs and foxes behave in much the same way. For example, to bury excess food or bones, they dig a small hole using their fore-paws, drop the food into the hole, and then cover it by pushing sand or soil over it with sweeping movements of the muzzle. This behaviour is so ingrained that wolves raised on concrete floors will perform all the bury-ing movements, including digging and muzzle sweeping, even when there is no soil available. Scent marking is another pattern which is seen in all the wild canids and should also be familiar to anyone who has watched domestic dogs on their daily rounds, carefully sniffing every tree, stone, and lamp post, then lifting a leg and urin-ating over each object. Dogs gain much in-formation from these marks including the numbers and sexes of other dogs in the neighbourhood and the presence of any females on heat. In fact, the odour of each individual's urine probably has special characteristics which make it easily identi-fiable to another dog in much the same way that humans can identify each other by their fingerprints and voices.

Hunting dictates behaviour

In the Canidae, some of the most interesting differences between species are in social behaviour, and these seem to have evolved in connection with the two main types of hunting. Most of the smaller fox-like species (but also the large maned wolf which is basically an overgrown fox) prey on small rats, mice, and rabbits. They hunt alone and live a solitary life except during the breeding season. To keep in touch with other foxes, they rely upon smell and sound since the olfactory and auditory senses are best for long-distance contact. Like the odour of their urine, the calls of foxes differ from individual to individual, but they also change from season to season so males and females have special calls before mating and when rearing cubs.

The large wolves, on the other hand, have become co-operative hunters and prey on big game like deer, elk, and moose. They must live in close contact the year round, and in order to maintain good relationships within the group, they have developed a much more complex way of communicating with each other than the solitary foxes and have also learned to adjust their behaviour to the needs of the group. In a group of wolves there is a hierarchy or peck order, and each individual must make certain ges-tures and assume certain postures to inform other group members of his status and mood. These visual signals are frequently repeated so the wolves are constantly re-minded of everyone's position in the rank order, and if any wolf decides to challenge the authority of the leader, the entire group is aware of it immediately.

Doing the foxtrot? In the mating season foxes frequently engage in play. They 'mouth' each other, coming close together with wide open mouths, then they rise up onto hindlegs and put forepaws on each other's shoulders. Although they move about they are not performing a dance. The high-pitched yapping heard around their homes in spring is a prelude to this.

Language of the dogs

The movements of tail, ears, and mouth and the overall body posture are the main components of the canid visual language. In foxes, these movements are simple; a wide-opened mouth, waving tail, and tightly pulled-back ears signify threat. They also raise their hackles, but since the fur is rela-tively short, it is not as conspicuous as in the maned wolf which has a black stripe along the back which contrasts with the russet fur on the rest of the body. Jackals are more sociable than foxes. Although they do not ordinarily hunt in packs, they do occasionally congregate to feed on carcases left by larger predators like lions. Their ear and mouth movements are similar to those of the foxes, but they have developed more controlled tail movements for communi-cating with other jackals. They can wag their tails to indicate friendliness and can also hold the tail in an up or down position de-pending how confident or afraid they are. The side-striped jackal, a species from Central Africa, has a white tip on its tail which emphasizes these movements; most of the other jackals as well as wolves and coyotes have black tail tips instead.

The wolves, wild dogs, and coyotes use the same ear and tail movements as the jackals. In addition, they have very complicated facial expressions which depend on three separate movements of the mouth. Two of these in a simplified form are also seen in jackals and foxes, a retraction of the corners of the mouth to indicate submission, and an opening of the mouth to indicate excite-ment, but the third, the snarl, is a specia-lization of the very social species. During a snarl, the lips are raised to expose the dan-gerous canine teeth; this is usually seen only in animals about to attack. Thus the wolves, coyotes and dogs have developed a signal to warn their fellows if they are feeling aggres-sive which, like an air-raid siren, gives the victim time to begin his escape. The victim can also, however, stop an attack by assum-ing a very submissive posture, turning over on his back, tucking his tail between his legs, pulling back his mouth corners in a submissive 'grin', and spreading his ears apart at the base which makes him look smaller and gives the face a smooth flat appearance. The fact that an aggressive wolf is not only inhibited from biting group members in a submissive posture but also gives a preliminary warning before attack-ing is an important method by which argu-ments among wolves are prevented from becoming serious and perhaps from leading to bloodshed. Also, this very complicated visual language enables group members to 'converse' with less misunderstanding than humans, where so often the facial expres-sion conveys a meaning which is the exact opposite of what is said.

Joe Van Wormer: Photo Res

Zool Soc London

△ *Looking daggers: a snarl from a coyote, exposing the dangerous canine teeth, is a most obviously threatening expression which provides ample warning for its fellows.*
▷ *Two South American maned wolves in battle. The white fur on the inside of their ears is exposed when the ears are pulled back during a threat. They also raise their hackles, made more prominent by the dark stripe along their backs.*
▽ *As well as for the more mundane tasks of sledge drawing, Eskimos use huskies on hunting expeditions. Too much bravado, however, can have disastrous consequences when the quarry is as formidable as this polar bear.*

Fred Bruemmer

Butterfly courtship

Most of us enjoy watching butterflies as they feed from flowers in the garden, flutter along a country lane or glide from one sun-lit glade to another in a woodland clearing. When it comes to observing their more intricate flight patterns, however, very few people realise that what they are watching is often the ritual of courtship.

The sensational aerobatics of two green hairstreak butterflies are not just a show of spring exuberance but almost certainly the preliminary flights before courtship and mating take place. So difficult is this behaviour to watch high up against a brilliant spring sky, however, that as far as I know no one has ever analysed it. I believe it could be recorded by slow motion camera and it certainly calls out to be put on film. In this same way the fluttering zig-zag chase of the brilliant azure male adonis blue, as it pursues a dusky female of its species up and down the slopes on chalk and limestone downs, is again only the preliminary to the final frenzied fluttering as the two insects scramble about on the turf until the male manages to manoeuvre the female into a position which makes mating possible.

It is easier to study courtship behaviour among the larger butterflies and Dr Niko Tinbergen was first in the field with his remarkable study of the grayling butterfly and its extraordinary courtship. Once the male has found a willing female he begins ritual movements in front of her, opening and closing his wings, and waving his antennae. The courtship is completed by the grayling raising high his forewings without moving his body so that he appears to execute a deep bow. An interesting discovery during experiments was that a male will court a dead female and that once the courtship starts the male continues the ritual even if the female is removed.

Perhaps the easiest family to watch are the vanessas—for example, the peacock, the small tortoiseshell and the painted lady. In the early spring, on awakening from hibernation, two or three peacock butterflies will establish their territory in some sunny sheltered place, often a pathway beside a wood, and for several weeks they will patrol this beat, each day elaborating their courtship ritual. After the 'warming up' flights, the female will sit on the bare earth while one or other of the males alights beside her and walks around her, brushing her body with his wings.

A protracted mating

The small tortoiseshell also has a long period of vigorous flight in a restricted area, but when settled, the sexes sit opposite each other, the male butterfly tapping the antennae of the female with his own. If the female is responsive she will allow this to go on for several minutes; if not she will at once take to the wing and the chase continues. The culmination of the small tortoiseshell's courtship was first observed by the late Mr Prideau of Brasted, Kent. He was a supreme student of the habits of butterflies and after watching a pair of these tawny butterflies all through one hot spring day he noticed, in the late afternoon, that the female appeared to be searching for something on a grassy bank. Suddenly the butterfly disappeared under an overhanging tussock of grass and was immediately followed by the male. Mr Prideau marked the spot and on returning at dusk he found the butterflies there, still mated, sitting tail to tail.

On arrival in England from North Africa in early summer the painted ladies invariably make for the nearest hilltop or stretch of downland and there they start their wild courtship flight—wide sweeps in a figure of eight—backwards and forwards over the same patch of ground. The artist Vere Temple, who studied the behaviour of butterflies for her work, likened this to a ballet sequence. I have watched it on several occasions on the north downs of Kent where I now live, but I have never seen the finish of this 'dance', or found a mated pair. Maybe the butterflies return to the lowlying fields and meadows before this takes place.

I have bred a great many butterflies in captivity and it always puzzled me that while I could induce the common clouded yellow to mate quite easily I never succeeded in getting a pairing of the rarer pale clouded yellow in a breeding cage or laying tub. The female, after feeding from flowers, would fly up towards the light and cling to the netting. Very soon a male would follow and they would flutter around each other, and then invariably, when I thought mating was very near, the female would drop down to the bottom of the cage and remain there quiescent. The male would continue to flutter around for a few minutes, then lose interest and return to feed on the flowers.

The mystery explained

Then one August I happened to be in the Isle of Thanet, Kent, collecting butterflies. My stay coincided with the emergence of a large local brood of these migrants which had arrived earlier in the summer and had colonized the whole area. As I walked among the purple flowers of the lucern I noticed, every now and then, how one of the much paler females would leave the flowers and ascend in fairly tight spirals to a considerable height in the sky, but at first the significance of this did not strike me. Then I realised that quite often one or more of the bright yellow males would follow in pursuit. On shading my eyes I could follow what was happening. It was some time before I spotted a pair come tumbling down close together right down to the ground. By the time I had pushed through the lucern to the spot where they had alighted the pair had mated. My failure to breed them in captivity was now explained. It was clear that they needed the stimulation of free, high flight before they would mate.

The easiest of all the butterflies to observe from a distance are the cabbage whites, because their light colouring makes them conspicuous, and they are usually quite common. On a sunny summer's day one can sometimes see a female chased by several males, all of them following her flight pattern as if they were strung together on an invisible thread. Finally the female will settle and one of the males will quickly mate with her. If the pair are disturbed the male will take to the wing, carrying the female with him. If swallowtail butterflies are disturbed while mating it is invariably the female that carries the male.

Why there should be this distinction in behaviour between different species has not, as yet, been explained.

▽ *Common swallowtail butterflies hang precariously from a flower during mating.*

▽ *A courting couple of clouded yellows cavort on a thistle, a preamble to mating.*

▷ *A bird's-foot trefoil provides two common blue butterflies with a nuptial venue.*

F Baillie · NHPA

The geography of animals

Zoogeography combines animals with maps and tries to account for the past and present pattern of animal distribution throughout the world. Most animals are limited to definite areas of the world. Cosmopolitan forms such as the rat have taken advantage of man's transportation systems, being carried in ships, aircraft and ground transport. Rodents are, however, extremely adaptable animals and their enormous breeding capacity and omnivorous diet must have contributed to the successful colonisation of new areas.

Apart from these 'super' forms, most other types are limited from spreading geographically by barriers like the sea. Terrestrial or freshwater animals must undergo extreme adaptation to exist in the sea. The reverse situation also holds true for many marine animals. Other barriers include mountains, temperature and rainfall. Here we deal with three quite distinct zoogeographical regions.

This chart shows the world occurrence of land vertebrate families in the six faunal regions first described by 19th century zoologists. 1 Palearctic region, including Europe, North Africa and Asia except the south and southeast. Not very rich in varieties of animals. The fauna is a complex of Old World tropical and New World temperate families because of interchange with the Nearctic over the intermittent Bering Strait land bridge. 2 Nearctic region, including North America, Greenland and Iceland. Contains New World tropical and Old World temperate families. Sometimes grouped with the Palearctic region as the Holarctic. 3 Neotropical region, including most of Central America and all of South America. Rich in endemic vertebrates, and shares families with the Nearctic. 4 Ethiopian region, Africa south of the Sahara. Has the most varied vertebrate fauna of any region. 5 Oriental region, including southern Asia from Persia to Burma and southeast Asia, together with some of the Malay Archipelago. 6 Australasian region, including Australia, New Zealand and the rest of the Malay Archipelago.

Distribution table

Common names	Families	Palearctic	Nearctic	Neotropical	Ethiopian	Oriental	Australian
rabbits	*Leporidae*	■	■	■	■	■	■
mice	*Muridae & Cricetidae*	■	■	■	■	■	■
dogs	*Canidae*	■	■	■	■	■	■
bats	*Order: Chiroptera (17 families)*	■	■	■	■	■	■
shrews	*Soricidae*	■	■	■	■	■	
squirrels	*Sciuridae*	■	■	■	■	■	
stoat, badger, skunk, etc.	*Mustellidae*	■	■	■	■	■	
cats	*Felidae*	■	■	■	■	■	
bears	*Ursidae*	■	■	■		■	
deer	*Cervidae*	■	■	■		■	
cattle, antelope, sheep & goats	*Bovidae*	■	■		■	■	
hedgehogs	*Erinaceidae*	■			■	■	
porcupines	*Hystricidae*	■			■	■	
civets	*Viverridae*	■			■	■	
hyenas	*Hyaenidae*	■			■	■	
pigs	*Suidae*	■			■	■	
pandas & racoons	*Procyonidae*		■	■		■	
dormice	*Gliridae*	■			■		
jerboas	*Dipodidae*	■			■		
hyraxes	*Procaviidae*	■			■		
horses	*Equidae*	■			■		
moles	*Talpidae*	■	■				
beavers	*Castoridae*	■	■				
jumping mice	*Zapodidae*	■	■				
camels & llamas	*Camelidae*	■		■			
mole rat	*Spalacidae*	■					
selevinia	*Seleviniidae*	■					
hedgesparrows	*Prunellidae*	■					
pocket gophers	*Geomyidae*		■				
pocket mice & kangaroo rats	*Heteromyidae*		■				
mountain beaver	*Aplodontidae*		■				
pronghorns	*Antilocapridae*		■				
turkey	*Meleagrididae*		■				
gila monsters	*Helodermatidae*		■				
garpikes	*Amiidae*		■				
bowfins	*Lepisosteidae*		■				
tapirs	*Tapiridae*			■		■	
anteaters	*Myrmecophagidae*			■			
sloths	*Bradypodidae*			■			
armadillos	*Dasypodidae*		▲	■			
mouse-like marsupials	*Caenolestidae*			■			
opossums	*Didelphidae*		▲	■			
New World monkeys	*Cebidae*			■			
marmosets & tarmarins	*Callithricidae*			■			
tree porcupines	*Erethizontidae*		▲	■			
capybaras	*Hydrochaeridae*			■			
guinea pigs	*Caviidae*			■			
agoutis	*Dasyproctidae*			■			
pacas	*Cuniculidae*			■			
coypus	*Capromyidae*			■			
chinchillas	*Chinchillidae*			■			

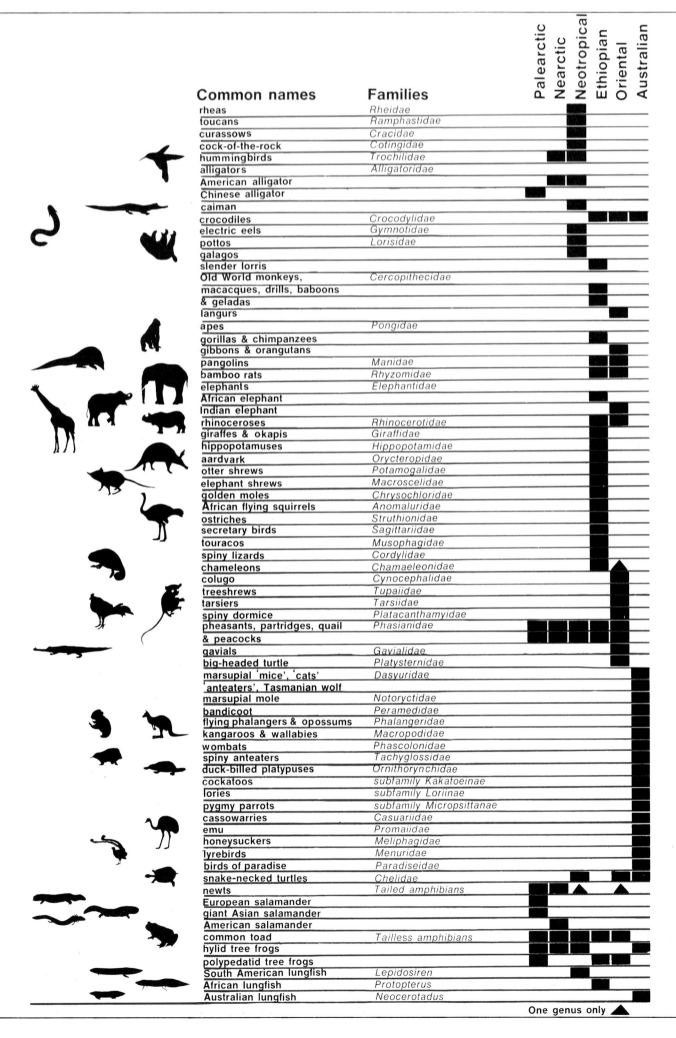

Research: Maurice Burton and Martin Jones

Design: David Eldred

South American animals

South America has an amazing number of different kinds of animals. This is due to the wide variation of habitats, as shown on the map, and partly because of the continent's long period of isolation before the land bridge between North and South America was re-established in the comparatively recent Pleistocene era about 1 million years ago. During the long separation, many strange creatures evolved, some quite unlike any others in the world and some so similar that all sorts of theories (such as drifting continents and floating rafts) have been put forward to explain such convergences. For example, the porcupine-like rodents—cavies, agoutis and coypu—nearly all live in South America but the Old World porcupine and its relatives live in Africa and parts of Asia. The two groups are very similar in their anatomy but there is no fossil evidence to suggest how they might have spread from one continent to the other or even that they had a common ancestor. The related capybara, the largest living rodent, is found near water all over South America, unlike the mara and the plains viscacha which are at home only on the pampa grasslands.

Marsupials are generally found in Australia only but a family of marsupials occurs in the forest of Central and northern South America. Moreover, one of them, the common American opossum, is also to be found on the pampa, and it is remarkable how this animal has adapted its behaviour so well to different habitats although it is primarily a tree-dweller. Of course, the obvious mammalian denizens of the forest areas are the New World monkeys of the family Cebidae. These squirrel monkeys, spider monkeys, tamarins and marmosets travel acrobatically through the trees in groups, noisily chattering and calling. Sloths, however, move very slowly and seem to spend most of their time hanging upside down on branches—much as does the dreaded anaconda which lies in wait for any passing prey and then squeezes it to death in its coils.

Giants and fairies

Ants and termites, of which there are a great many species in South America, are preyed on by several mammals and birds such as the primitive antbirds and antpipits and the small anteater, or tamandua, and the giant armadillo. The fairy armadillo and the giant anteater live in more open countryside and the former eats roots as well, while its larger cousin the hairy armadillo will eat anything. In spite of their heavy armour, armadillos move surprisingly swiftly and if they are cornered they just curl up and wait until the danger has passed — such danger ranges from man to mustelids. The latter are represented by the skunk, the tyra and the grisson which are well distributed and will eat anything that they can get hold of including the many lizards, frogs and toads which abound wherever there is any standing water.

In the great Amazon and the other extensive river systems in South America live many crocodiles and caimans, the dreaded piranha fish and electric eels which can give a nasty shock although their efforts are normally directed towards other fish. Catfish and the strange four-eyed fish are unique to this faunal region, as is the lungfish *Lepidosiren* which has existed virtually unchanged for 350 million years.

It is strange that in South America there are no really large ungulates like the elephant, hippopotamus and rhinoceros of Africa. Indeed, there is only one odd-toed ungulate—the Brazilian tapir, but the artiodactyls are well represented by the peccary, various deer such as the pudu, the pampas deer and the huemal and by the camelids. These supercilious-looking beasts (llamas, alpacas, guanacoes and vicunas) once lived all over the pampa and mountain slopes, but they have been much hunted for their very fine wool. The beautiful chinchilla is also on the verge of extinction in its native habitat in the high Andes because its fine fur is the most valuable pelt in the world.

Hawks and hummingbirds

The llamids, like the flightless rhea of the pampa, rely on their speed to outwit enemies and the young have to be able to run with the herd a few days after birth. Any that cannot keep up are victims of the watchful puma, fox or maned wolf and the large Andean condors are not slow to arrive at a recent kill. Eagles, hawks and owls are well represented in the mountainous regions but on the pampa the comanch and chimang hawks hold nearly absolute sway. Only the little burrowing owl escapes their attention;

he lives with the viscacha colonies and feeds on small mice and insects.

A kaleidoscope of over 200 bird species visits the pampa for overwintering or breeding, but the tropical Amazon forests are the permanent home of many birds, including dainty hummingbirds and colourful but noisy parrots and toucans. Surprisingly, parrots and hummingbirds are found as far south as Patagonia. The strange tropical forest bird the hoatzin is quite unlike any other known bird. If it should fall into water it can swim well and once the bank has been reached it climbs up the nearest tree by clinging onto the bark—not by the feet like a woodpecker but by means of claws on the wings!

The most famous winged animals of South America are the vampire bats. They are found as far south as northern Argentina and are extremely dangerous to domestic animals and man, not because of the amount of blood which they suck but because of the diseases and infections which they transmit through the wound. Other dangerous bites are those from the several poisonous snakes and spiders which occupy a variety of habitats. The pampa coral snakes are very beautiful to look at but their bite is one of the most feared in the world.

The number and types of insect species in South America have not yet been fully recorded, apart from the bees and mosquitoes, which are of obvious economic importance. But one insect that has achieved world-wide acclaim is the cactus moth of the pampa. This, apparently insignificant moth was successfully introduced into Australia to combat the cacti which were rapidly overrunning the country.

The stories of the cactus and of the rabbit in Australia clearly indicate the danger of introducing foreign species into a country. Not only do the new species form a threat in themselves, but they may compete with native species—sometimes to the point of extinction of the originals. In South America where the native fauna is so unqiue this is a very real danger. The introduced European hare has ousted the mara from the Pampa, and the red fox and the red deer have pushed the native foxes and deer into inhospitable areas. Unless steps are taken to prevent such extermination by introduced species and by man himself, the rich and varied fauna of South America will have disappeared even before much of it has been identified and studied.

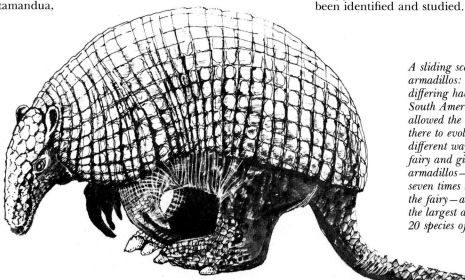

A sliding scale of armadillos: the widely differing habitats of South America have allowed the animals there to evolve in many different ways. The fairy and giant armadillos—the giant seven times the size of the fairy—are respectively the largest and smallest of 20 species of armadillo.

South America is like an enormous triangle with one of the world's longest mountain barriers running down its western edge, the Andes, and the world's biggest river, the Amazon, and largest tropical rain forest in its northern half. It is a land of surprising contrasts in vegetation. Rain forests, snow-capped mountains, and very dry deserts are all found in the tropical area. To the south are glaciers, grasslands, the cold, wind-blown arid wastes of Patagonia and the desolate islands of Tierra del Fuego. The amazing number of different animals that live there are due to the wide variation in vegetation and also the result of the continent's long period of separation from North America when many strange creatures evolved.

sloth
cotton-headed marmoset
hoatzin
opossum
Brazilian tapir
anaconda

puma
grisson
tyra
capybara
anis
antbirds
hummingbirds
parrots
toucans
crocodile
piranha fish
electric eel
lungfish
monkeys

deciduous forest

maned wolf
jaguar
hummingbird

vampire
puma
parrots
toucans
ants
capybara
electric eel
sloth
harpy eagle

pampas

giant anteater
plains viscacha
rhea

pampas deer
coral snakes
chimango hawk
burrowing owl

mountain range

mountain viscacha
vicuna
chinchilla

Andean condor
llama
guanaco

Patagonia

mara
Magellan penguin
tucotuco

burrowing parrot
elephant seal
guanaco

The fauna of New Zealand

New Zealand is an 'ancient island' that has been isolated from the rest of the world for many millions of years, if not always. As a result, much of New Zealand's plant and animal life is unique. On the one hand, there are species such as the flightless kiwis and the now extinct moas that evolved there in isolation; on the other, there are species such as the tuatara and the New Zealand frogs *Leiopelma*, representing survival pockets of animals once widespread but now extinct elsewhere.

This long isolation has meant that the fauna has evolved in the absence of predatory animals. Consequently, the dominant vertebrates—birds—have shown a strong tendency to occupy terrestrial habitats. Many, such as the kiwi, moa, kakapo, weka and takahe have become flightless, and others, such as the fernbird, saddleback and rockwren, appear to be becoming so.

The only mammals native to New Zealand are two species of bat. One, the long-tailed bat, is a representative of an Australian genus *Chalinolobus*, but the other, the short-tailed bat *Mystacina* is endemic and has a number of unique characteristics that makes its relationship to other bats obscure. This bat is undoubtedly a very early coloniser of New Zealand.

Reptile relics

Two families of reptiles are represented in New Zealand: the tuatara *Sphenodon* and the skinks and geckos. The tuatara, whose relatives flourished during the age of reptiles and died out some 135 million years ago, has been described as a living fossil. It is extinct on the mainland but survives on a number of small offshore island sanctuaries. It is a stocky reptile, up to 20 in. long and is notable for a number of remarkable anatomical features. One is the presence of a third, or pineal 'eye' situated in the top of the skull, which seems to be sensitive to heat. The tuatara lays eggs which take about a year to hatch. Its metabolism is very slow and indications are that the tuatara has a life span of at least 200–300 years. The skinks and geckos are represented by some 2 dozen species, and the geckos are unique in that they are ovoviviparous and do not lay eggs as do all other geckos.

Amphibia are represented by only three species of frog *Leiopelma* which are the most primitive known forms of frogs and toads. All are extremely rare and of restricted distribution. They have a modified life history in that the tadpole stage is by-passed, with the eggs hatching directly into small froglets, and this seems to be related to their habitat which—particularly in the Stephen's Island frog—is restricted to small areas of mossy stones far removed from water.

Birds dominate

Birds are by far the dominant element of the New Zealand faunal scene. Most of them are of relatively recent origin and have arrived as a result of occasional and accidental importation via the west wind drift—a process that is still going on today. The last few years, for example, have seen the arrival and establishment of the Australian

△△ *The tuatara is still found on small offshore island sanctuaries. It is the only surviving member of a family which flourished in the age of reptiles—some 135 million years ago.*
△ *The weka* **Gallirallus australis**, *a chicken-sized rail, is flightless despite its well-developed wings. It is a forest dweller, nesting in burrows or under a tussock of grass.*

spur-winged plover, the Australian coot, the black-fronted dotterel and the welcome swallow, to mention but a few. The ancient element of the New Zealand avi-fauna is represented by a number of endemic orders, genera and species. Among the most notable are the kiwis which are nocturnal, flightless birds with rudimentary wings and no tails. The New Zealand wattlebirds include the now extinct huia which was unique among birds in that the sexes had bills of different lengths that were used in different ways, and the now rare saddleback, suddenly in jeopardy as a result of recent predation by rats on small surviving island populations. Also of ancient lineage are the recently re-discovered takahe: robust, heavily built, flightless relatives of the purple gallinules, and the New Zealand wrens—which counted among their number a small population of a distinct form, the Stephen's Island wren, now extinct (1894), that may have been the only flightless

passerine known. It was confined to a small island in Cook Strait, led a terrestrial existence and was never seen to fly.

Three parrots are endemic—the kea, the kaka and the kakapo. The kea is notorious for its reputed attacks on sheep. The kakapo, a large, nocturnal, virtually flightless bird is verging on extinction and at the present time is the subject of a project designed to save the species by breeding the birds in captivity, as yet without success. Another unique New Zealand species is the wry-billed plover—the only known bird with a lateral bend to its bill.

Being an isolated island group, New Zealand is a focal point for a large number of sea birds. Eleven of the world's penguins are on the New Zealand list, 10 albatrosses, 46 petrels and some 14 shags. Also conspicuous are the immense numbers of Arctic waders that 'winter' around New Zealand's coastline. The commonest are bar-tailed godwits, turnstones, golden plovers and knots but over 30 species have been seen.

No account of New Zealand bird-life would be complete without some reference to the impact of man and his camp followers on this long-isolated birds' paradise. The story begins with the Polynesian voyagers who brought with them the Polynesian dog and the kiore or Maori rat. The kiore has proved relatively harmless but the Polynesian dog undoubtedly wrought havoc among ground birds, particularly the kakapo. Polynesian man himself, it is now known, was responsible for the final extinction of the moas. Of 27 accepted species, the bones of 22 have been found in association with Polynesian middens and hunting camps.

Immigrant upset

The arrival of Europeans during the 19th century saw large areas of forest cleared and swamps drained. Habitats were altered and inevitably the numbers of many forest living birds were reduced. Yet the number of extinctions was small; the huia was the most notable example. On the other hand, birds such as the saddleback that became extinct on the mainland but survived, so it was thought, on offshore islands, are now threatened by population explosions of rats and other introduced predators.

Along with the clearance and drainage of land man introduced large numbers of exotic species: rats of three kinds, cats, dogs, mustelids, opossums, several varieties of deer, chamois, thar, wallabies, rabbits, hedgehogs, 36 species of bird, trout, salmon—and even Australian frogs! Inevitably this mixed bag has had repercussions on the native ecology. There is evidence, however, that of recent years many of the native birds are staging a 'come-back', occupying man-made habitats and moving into exotic vegetation, and the picture today is by no means as gloomy as it was 50 years ago.

Space prevents mention of New Zealand's many forms of primitive insect life. Nor can full reference be made to conservation policies, national parks and the many and varied island sanctuaries. Suffice it to say that in the Wildlife Section of the Internal Affairs Department, New Zealand has workers actively employed in the conservation of New Zealand's unique wildlife heritage.

After the Invasion

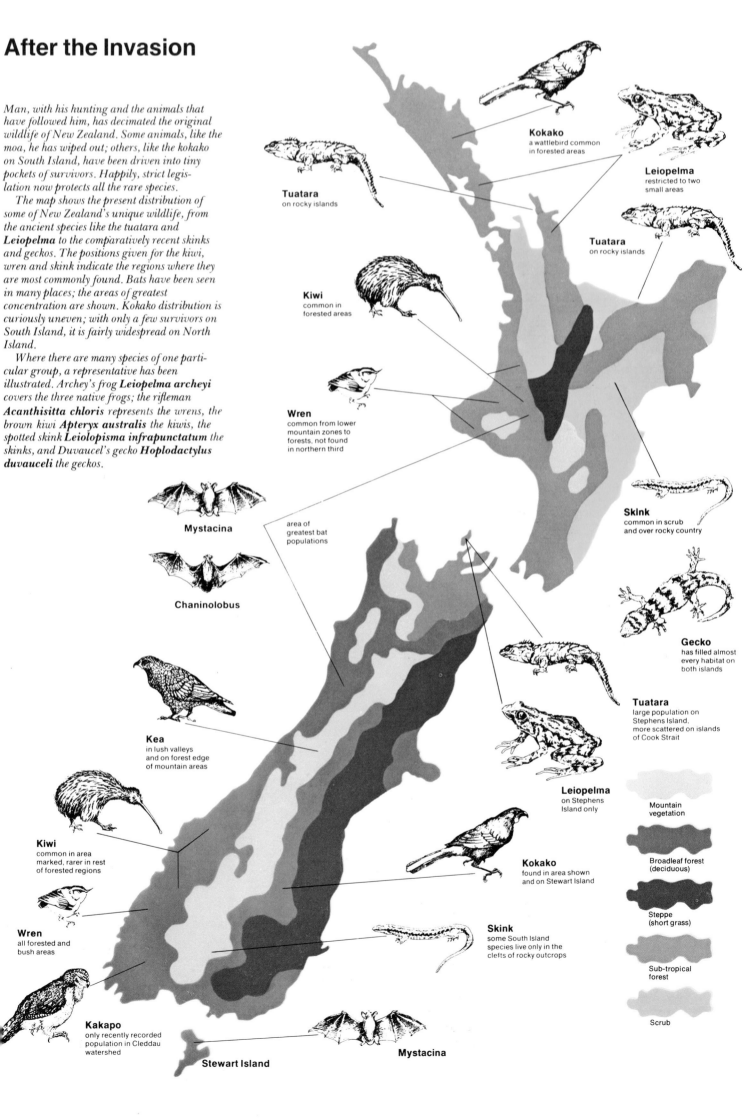

Man, with his hunting and the animals that have followed him, has decimated the original wildlife of New Zealand. Some animals, like the moa, he has wiped out; others, like the kokako on South Island, have been driven into tiny pockets of survivors. Happily, strict legislation now protects all the rare species.

The map shows the present distribution of some of New Zealand's unique wildlife, from the ancient species like the tuatara and **Leiopelma** to the comparatively recent skinks and geckos. The positions given for the kiwi, wren and skink indicate the regions where they are most commonly found. Bats have been seen in many places; the areas of greatest concentration are shown. Kokako distribution is curiously uneven; with only a few survivors on South Island, it is fairly widespread on North Island.

Where there are many species of one particular group, a representative has been illustrated. Archey's frog **Leiopelma archeyi** covers the three native frogs; the rifleman **Acanthisitta chloris** represents the wrens, the brown kiwi **Apteryx australis** the kiwis, the spotted skink **Leiolopisma infrapunctatum** the skinks, and Duvaucel's gecko **Hoplodactylus duvauceli** the geckos.

Kokako
a wattlebird common in forested areas

Leiopelma
restricted to two small areas

Tuatara
on rocky islands

Tuatara
on rocky islands

Kiwi
common in forested areas

Wren
common from lower mountain zones to forests, not found in northern third

Skink
common in scrub and over rocky country

Mystacina

area of greatest bat populations

Chaninolobus

Gecko
has filled almost every habitat on both islands

Tuatara
large population on Stephens Island, more scattered on islands of Cook Strait

Kea
in lush valleys and on forest edge of mountain areas

Leiopelma
on Stephens Island only

Kiwi
common in area marked, rarer in rest of forested regions

Kokako
found in area shown and on Stewart Island

Wren
all forested and bush areas

Skink
some South Island species live only in the clefts of rocky outcrops

Kakapo
only recently recorded population in Cleddau watershed

Stewart Island

Mystacina

Mountain vegetation

Broadleaf forest (deciduous)

Steppe (short grass)

Sub-tropical forest

Scrub

The Galapagos

'As I was walking along I met two large tortoises, each of which must have weighed at least 200 pounds: one was eating a piece of cactus, as I approached, it stared at me and slowly stalked away; the other gave me a deep hiss, and drew in its head. These huge reptiles, surrounded by the black lava, the leafless shrubs, and large cacti, seemed to my fancy like some antediluvian animals.' Darwin's account of his visit to the 'Enchanted Isles' of the Galapagos in his *Voyage of the Beagle* in 1835 shows his growing conviction of the mechanism of evolution. These volcanic islands, lying 600 miles off Ecuador on the equator, had been frequently visited by buccaneers and whalers. They likewise reported the bizarre animals they found, describing the prehistoric-looking iguanas, the flightless cormorant and the tame doves.

Like other volcanic and oceanic islands, the Galapagos harbour a unique fauna and flora. Few species chanced to reach these barren islands, but the original colonization by hardy plants was perhaps a seed carried by a bird or one blown there by the wind. Likewise perhaps a few animals from the South American continent drifting on balsa logs were swept by the Humboldt current up onto the lava rock. Occasional reptiles and mammals landed on these shores, and with a new environment, lack of competitors and no predators they evolved independently from their ancestors. No amphibians were able to withstand such a journey because of their permeable skin but reptiles and mammals were. The only endemic species of the latter class are a bat and a rat, though recent introduction of goats, pigs, cattle, donkeys and dogs has altered the original balance.

Birds have the least difficulty in colonizing new territory and so are abundant. 'Darwin's finches' are the most common: there are 14 species. The ancestors of each species must have been isolated for many thousands of years, adapting to their particular niche. Finally, when meeting again, they were either able to survive together as separate species or were forced by competition to separate again unless the less well adapted species became extinct.

Variation of tortoises

The theory of evolution accounts for the variation of tortoises on the different islands. Galapagos is the name that the Spanish gave to these giant tortoises, and so the Archipelago has been named. Because of man's predation, tortoises are now found on only a few islands. An interesting relationship has grown up on some of the islands between these animals and the prickly pear *Opuntia* on which they feed. The tortoises eat the young plants and the lower hanging leaves of the tall cacti. *Opuntia* has evolved extra long spines on the young plants, and as they grow, a trunk is formed which is gradually covered by a thick 'bark'. The protective spines then fall off,

Caroline Weaver

△ *Blue-footed booby and young. These gannets range from Mexico and Peru to the Galapagos.*
▽ *Red rock crabs pulling at a carcase; thousands of these animals teem over the Galapagos shores.*

Caroline Weaver

so at either stage the tortoise is unable to eat the main part of the plant; but it still feeds on fallen leaves and pears. A further adaptation has taken place on certain islands—the tortoise's shell has become raised above the head, and the tortoise can stretch its neck higher to eat upper leaves.

Another species unique to the islands is the marine iguana. Colonies of these beasts, individuals of which grow up to 4 ft long, lie camouflaged and basking in the sun on the lava rock. When their temperature is raised and the tide is low, they swim out and feed on the algae on the rocks above and below the water. A related species but quite distinct is the land iguana, varying in colour from greyish-red to yellow. Also vegetarian, it feeds on fallen cacti, lichen and small succulent plants.

The Humboldt current from the Antarctic, which flows past these islands, has greatly influenced the climate, flora, and fauna. Penguins, perhaps carried from the Antarctic by chance, are found on the west coasts of certain islands, but surviving because of the cold water and the associated fish. Three species of booby live on these islands, as well as the man-o'-war bird. This scavenges and forces the boobies to give up or disgorge their fish. An albatross breeds on one island and can be seen skimming over the crests of the waves.

Volcanic camouflage

Many of the animals are camouflaged against the lava—the marine iguanas, the cormorant, the lava gull and the small Galapagos blue heron which searches through the rocks for small fish and crabs. Other species are far from camouflaged. The shy pink flamingo which inhabits the desolate lagoons is a distinct and easy target for a passing visitor. The bold and noisy mockingbird, varying in plumage from island to island, scavenges from animals and humans alike. The thousands of red rock crabs scramble across the rocks, and retreat into crevices, just to be heard as their claws rasp on the rocks below. Another characteristic of island fauna is the loss of colour, the male vermilion flycatcher is often seen paler than its female, and the finches exhibit no bright plumage.

The future of the Galapagos is uncertain. Introduced species are the greatest threat. Goats denude the earth. Pigs steal eggs of birds, tortoises and turtles. Brown and black rats from visiting boats now compete with the endemic rat. Man steals eggs, and in the past has captured tortoises, iguanas, fur seals and even birds for food, fur, and trophies, so several have become extinct or threatened with extinction. Animals on isolated islands are seldom naturally protected, and many are prone to grow very large. The lack of fear of man makes them fall easy prey. The final hope is that the Darwin Scientific Station set up by UNESCO will be able to control the introduced species, preserve those islands still uninhabited and prevent man from interfering any more than is necessary.

△ *Desolation row: Galapagos coast vegetation, with* **Opuntia**, *the prickly pear, in the foreground.*
◁ *Taking advantage of human settlement, a land iguana scavenges for food among pots and pans.*
▽ *The woodpecker finch* **Camarhynchus pallidus** *of the Galapagos probes for grubs with a cactus spine.*

Ecology

Animals and plants form a complex web of mutually dependent living systems. Ecology is the study of these systems in relation to the environment. Obvious ecological habitats are those formed by natural divisions. The shore, a boundary between land and sea, is a classical ecological zone. Other habitats are more difficult to define and must be described in terms of physical factors such as rainfall.

When a child visits a local pond he encounters a small yet definite ecological habitat. If he is observant he will notice the water insects, perhaps the most interesting members of the varied and abundant pond community. Many show fascinating adaptations of the respiratory system for aquatic life; devices for utilising the oxygen of pond water and various types of snorkels for breathing air at the surface.

Two articles in the Encyclopedia deal with opposite views of life in the seas. In the article on plankton we view the life of the uppermost pelagic zone through the magnified eye of the microscope. Plankton consists of minute green algae and the larval stages of vertebrate and invertebrate animals. Although much of the plankton has been identified and placed in various food chains, much still remains obscure.

From the surface plankton we plunge into the depths of the sea. This relatively inaccessible environment contains some mysterious animals. The twilight zone below 400 ft is inhabited by squid and fishes having complex arrays of light organs. In the deeper zones degenerate-looking fish swim with wide gaping mouths while long-legged invertebrates and eels probe the sea bed.

From the immense pressure and gloom of the deeps, we go to other harsh environments—the poles. Yet, despite the conditions prevailing in them, they show an amazing variety of life. Whereas the Antarctic consists of desolate wastes of ice and snow, winter and summer, the Arctic and surrounding areas contain a large number of species, and during the short summer flowers carpet the northern tundra.

Polar environments and life

Many people think the polar regions are confined to the areas within the Arctic and Antarctic circles. But they are much more extensive than this, and although the Arctic and Antarctic have no physical boundaries, they may be set apart by different states of climate—which consequently affect animal and plant life.

The Arctic is commonly defined as those northern areas in which the mean temperature for the warmest month—or isotherm—does not exceed 10°C. This isotherm closely coincides with the northern limit of tree growth, ranging from 60°N in Greenland, Alaska and Labrador to 72°N in Siberia, although it may be surpassed by dwarf birch and willow scrub. The major part of the Arctic is ocean, encircled by the northern coasts and offshore islands of North America, Greenland and Eurasia; no land lies beyond 83°N. Because the sea tones down the climate, producing relatively warm but short summers, most of the snow disappears from the extensive undulating plains and valleys. Conditions are suitable for the luxuriant growth of the perennial herbs and dwarf heath shrubs and the ferns, mosses, liverworts, and lichens, which make up the typical short 'tundra' vegetation. The Arctic lowlands have an equally rich and varied fauna.

In contrast, the Antarctic is a far more inhospitable region. It is essentially a continent, some 5·5 million square miles in area, with a mean elevation of 6 000 ft and a permanent ice-cap containing 90% of the world's snow and ice, in places exceeding 10 000 ft in thickness. The continent is surrounded by 12 million square miles of perpetually cold ocean. The Antarctic is usually thought of as all land south of the 60° parallel, but it also includes the South Sandwich Islands and Bouvet Island as far north as 55°S in the South Atlantic, on account of their cold climate and consequent biological poverty. Climatically, the Antarctic is considerably colder, windier, and more arid than the Arctic. Summer temperatures in the interior rarely rise above −20°C/−3°F and only in certain lowland coastal areas—particularly the Antarctic Peninsula and nearby islands—do summer

△ *Many low-lying headlands of the Antarctic which might otherwise support plant life, with its attendant animals, are rendered unsuitable by vast colonies of penguins.*
▷ *Part of the Arctic's wealth of animal life: a snow-hare. The Antarctic has few animals because of its isolation from land masses caused by a vast and perpetually cold ocean.*

temperatures rise marginally above freezing point to melt the snow. These localities provide sparse habitats for plants and animals. Such forms of life that exist must be adapted to survive the extremely exacting conditions. Antarctic vegetation is dominated by lichens, a few species of which grow on rock faces only 237 miles from the South Pole while wetter and more sheltered northerly areas support locally extensive stands of moss and lichen tundra vegetation. The most striking botanical difference between the north and south polar lands is that while there are about 900 species of vascular green plants in the Arctic—one-tenth of which occur at 83°N—the Antarctic has only two. Neither grow beyond 68°S.

Contrast in animals

The Antarctic's severe environment and impoverished flora is reflected in the ab-

animals live in fear of wolves. Land birds abound in the summer, ranging from numerous small birds (buntings, larks, pipits, wheatears, redpolls) to ptarmigan, ducks, geese and swans. They too fall victim to predators, including the snowy owl, peregrine and gyrfalcon.

Sea and shore birds are equally numerous, particularly gulls, ducks and waders, most of which are summer visitors. Although only 21 species of bird breed in the Antarctic, nine of which are petrels and six penguins, they are almost all highly gregarious in habit. Colonies of Adélie and chinstrap penguins may exceed a million inhabitants. In fact, many coastal habitats are rendered unsuitable for plant establishment by such densely populated colonies. Only the snow petrel is known to breed far inland. The only land bird, the sheathbill, scavenges along the shoreline and in penguin colonies

nutrients and plankton, the basic life form on which all marine food chains are dependent. Whereas in southern waters one group of fish, the nototheniids, is dominant, there are several important groups in the Arctic, including cod, herring and salmon. Fish and crustacea in turn provide food for the various species of seals, whales and seabirds. The scouring action of ice in the intertidal zone restricts marine vegetation to the deeper water where it provides habitats for a host of invertebrates.

The chief reasons for the differences in terrestrial life between the Arctic and Antarctic are fairly obvious. The Antarctic is essentially a high-altitude continent of ice, with an exceptionally cold and arid climate and separated from all other southern hemisphere land masses by a vast cold ocean. The fringe of the Arctic lands is either part of or close to the northern

In the more northerly parts of the Antarctic elephant seals spend the summer on the beaches, basking and sleeping in the weak sun.

R Lewis Smith

sence of terrestrial animal life. Natural selection has favoured only a small number of species, but those which have succeeded in adapting themselves exist in very large numbers, although virtually restricted to coastal habitats. The land fauna of the Antarctic contains a single bird species and a small number of invertebrates. On the other hand the Arctic has a wealth of mammal and bird species, although the cold-blooded reptiles and amphibians are not represented. Herds of herbivorous musk ox and caribou roam the tundra plains. Arctic and snowshoe hares and several species of lemming are preyed upon by ermine, weasels, and Arctic foxes, while all

whereas most other birds feed chiefly on small fish, crustacea and other marine life.

The largest of the true Antarctic land fauna is a tiny wingless fly *Belgica antarctica*, while several species of mites, ticks, and springtails, living among moss and under stones, complete the list of arthropods. The warm Arctic summer, however, brings forth swarms of flies, midges and mosquitoes, while beetles, bugs, bumblebees, butterflies and innumerable smaller species occur wherever there is lush vegetation.

Seas full of life

The polar seas are the most prolific in the world. They are unusually rich in chemical

continents, most of which are low-lying and snow-free in summer except for the Greenland ice-cap and mountainous regions. So there is no barrier preventing plants and animals from migrating north to occupy the wide range of available habitats. The abundance of fossil plants and coal beds in Antarctica provides evidence of a warm climate some 250—50 million years before the Pleistocene glaciers changed the continent to its present state. Post-glacial immigration by plants and animals has been greatly restricted by geographical isolation from the southern continents, meagre habitats and the understandable inability to adapt to the severe conditions.

Life in the deeps

Deep-sea fishes live in the open ocean, beyond the land-fringing waters that move over the continental shelves. They spend all or part of their life at depths where sunlight is faint or perpetually lacking. In the surface waters, down to a depth of about 300 ft in the clear ocean, the sun's rays are strong enough for photosynthesis by minute planktonic plants. Between depths of about 400 and 3 000 ft, again in the clearest waters, is a twilight zone which merges with underlying sunless waters. Since the mean depth of the deep-sea floor is close to 12 000 ft, most of the ocean must be sunless. Most kinds of deep-sea fishes live in the twilight zone: the deeper living kinds have been trawled at depths down to about 21 000 ft.

Though all deep-sea fishes live in dim or dark surroundings as adults, many kinds, particularly midwater forms, spend their early life in the productive surface waters, where there is enough planktonic food to nourish their larval stages. Moreover, many kinds of midwater fishes from the twilight zone migrate up each night to feed on the life of the surface layer. Before sunrise they swim down to the depths. One more qualification is also needed: the surroundings of deep-sea fishes are broken with flashes of living light, which are most frequent in the twilight zone. As we shall see, many kinds of deep-sea fishes have luminous organs: so do deep-sea squid, prawns, euphausiid shrimps, jellyfishes, salps, siphonophores, and so forth.

There are about 2 000 kinds of deep-sea fishes, but new species are described every year. Nearly a thousand species occupy the midwaters: the others live near or on the deep-sea floor. Over two-thirds of these forms live under the warm waters of the subtropical and tropical ocean between latitudes 40 degrees North and 40 degrees South.

Midwater fishes

The animals of the twilight zone form the mesopelagic fauna (about 750 species); below in the sunless water masses (about 3 000 – 9 000 ft) is a deep (bathypelagic) midwater fauna (about 150 species). There is a general idea about 'monsters of the deep', but most midwater fishes are less than a foot long.

In the twilight zone two-thirds of the fishes are either stomiatoids (about 300 species) or lanternfishes (Myctophidae, about 250 species). There are also alepisauroids, all predatory fishes with large jaws and teeth, giant swallowers (Chiasmodontidae) and melamphards. Some of the small stomiatoids and many lanternfishes, which feed largely on zooplankton, have silvery sides, but most of the predatory forms are dark brown or black. Light organs are developed on about three-quarters of the twilight zone species. These lights, which often form specific patterns, may well serve as recognition signs between members of particular species. In many lanternfishes and certain stomiatoids, some particular disposition of the light serves to distinguish the two sexes. To see these lights, and also to peer in dim surroundings, mesopelagic fishes tend to have large eyes, each with a wide pupil, large lens and a retina formed of very sensitive visual cells (rods). These fishes remind us of mice or owls. Lastly, many mesopelagic species, particularly lanternfishes, are prominent in the echo-traces called deep scattering layers.

The deeper, bathypelagic fauna consists largely of one division of anglerfishes, but the most numerous individuals are bristlemouths (see p 283). Bathypelagic fishes are predominantly black, and they lack complex light organ systems, such as characterize so many mesopelagic fishes. But the females of most anglerfishes develop an elaborate light organ at the end of a modified fin-ray, which emerges on top of the snout. In all probability, this light not only acts as a lure for their prey, but also attracts the males, which have no light and are much smaller (see p 52). Most dwarf male anglers have well developed eyes, but these are small in other bathypelagic fishes. Male anglers also have large olfactory organs.

Bottom-dwelling fishes

Many deep-sea photographs and observations from deep-diving underwater craft have now established that some fishes habitually swim over the deep-sea floor; the habit of the others is to rest on the bottom. Most kinds live over the continental slopes at depths between 600 and 4 500 ft. The deeper, abyssal species range down to depths of at least 21 000 ft.

The near-bottom swimmers are mostly rat-tails (Macrouridea), deep-sea cods (Moridae) and brotulids. There are also halosaurs, notacanths, eels (eg Synaphobranchidae), and small, dark-coloured sharks. They range in length from about 6 in. to 3 ft. The slope-dwelling species, like mesopelagic fishes, have large, sensitive eyes, which are small or degenerate in the abyssal forms. Much of their food consists of benthic invertebrates, particularly worms, and of crustaceans that swim near the bottom. Most species have a swimbladder, which is provided with drumming muscles in the males of many rat-tails and brotulids. Thus, these males presumably make sounds during sexual congress.

In polar and cold temperate waters, most kinds of fishes that rest on the bottom are either sea-snails (Diparidae) or eel-pouts (Zoarcidae). Under the warmer parts of the ocean, tripodfishes (Bathypteroidae) and chlorophthalmids are commoner. None of these fishes has a swimbladder, but the biology of benthic deep-sea fishes is not well known and remains an outstanding task in future exploration of the deep ocean, although research will reveal new information.

Key to facing page:

1 *Sunfish* 2 *Devilfish*
3 *Flying fish* 4 *Prawn*
5 *Plankton* 6 *Shark*
7 *Lantern fish* **Hygophum**
8 *Hatchet fish* **Sternoptyx diaphana**
9 *Melanostomiatid fish* **Grammatostomias**
10 *Deep-sea squid* **Pherygioteuthis giardi**
11 *Hatchet fish* **Argyro pelecus gigas**
12 *Gonostomatid* **Vinciguerria**
13 *Shrimp* **Notostomus**
14 *Stomiatoid* **Idiacanthus niger**
15 *Deep-sea squid* **Histioteuthis**
16 *Stomiatoid fish. Large swallower* **Chauliodus**
17 *Pelagic tunicate* **Pyrosoma**
18 *Gonostomatid* **Cyclothone microdon**
19 *Gonostomatid* **Cyclothone pallida**
20 *Siphonophore* **Stephanomia**
21 *Deep-sea octopod* **Amphitretus**
22 *Deep-sea medusa* **Atolla**
23 *Ceratoid anglerfish* **Linophryne arborifera**
24 *Ceratoid anglerfish* **Melanocetus johnsoni**
25 *Ceratoid anglerfish* **Lasiognathus saccostoma**
26 *Bob-tailed snipe eel* **Cyema atrum**
27 *Deep-sea mysid shrimp* **Gnathophausia**
28 *Gulper eel* **Eurypharynx pelecanoides**
29 *Sea spider* **Colossendeis**
30 *Rat-tail* **Nezumia**
31 *Deep-sea eel* **Synaphobranchus**
32 *Eryonoid* **Polycheles typhlops**

shallow coastal water   oceanic water

continental shelf

deep sea begins

twilight zone

400 ft

3000 ft

continental slope

bathypelagic (midwater) zone

9000 ft
deep sea benthos

Lynda Brockbank

There are two sharply contrasted living spaces in the ocean, the shallow coastal waters which lie over the continental shelf and the great water masses which fill the oceanic provinces. The oceanic waters are the habitat of many groups of varied animals; some of which are discussed above.

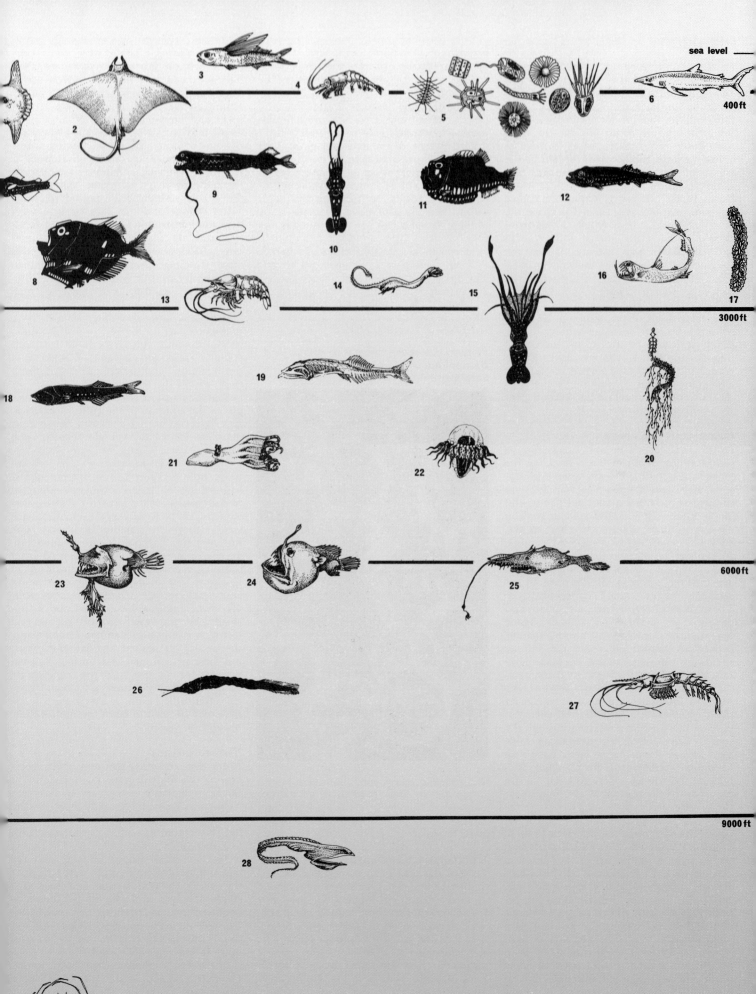

sea level

400 ft

2

3

4

5

6

8

9

10

11

12

13

14

15

16

17

3000 ft

18

19

20

21

22

23

24

25

6000 ft

26

27

9000 ft

28

29

30

31

32

12000 ft

Plankton

Plankton is a word of Greek derivation meaning literally 'that which drifts'. For this reason the term is applied to aerial, fresh-water or saltwater drifting inhabitants. In this instance, though, we are going to consider the marine forms—by far the most spectacular and colourful of all 'drifters'.

Just because these creatures drift at the mercy of the great oceanic currents, the rapid shoreline undertows and the wind-blown surface currents, it does not follow that they are inactive. Indeed perhaps the most noticeable feature of a plankton sample is that every animal quivers, jerks and undulates with activity. Under the microscope the swimming movements often seem efficient and fast. Nonetheless the progress, when compared with the forces and speeds of oceanic currents, is very limited indeed. Some of the more capable swimmers do, however, manage to migrate vertically and so pass from one current of water to another. In this way, by dropping from, say, an east-going current into a lower west-going current, the tiny animal can 'ride' the currents to maintain its position over the sea floor or control its drift.

Community members

Drifting animals, large and small, may be found at any depth in the oceans, but the majority are confined to the upper one hundred or so feet. Plankton communities are comprised of both animals and plants, and in the same way that land animals feed on plant growth or upon each other, so also do these small highly specialized drifters. In general the plant members of the community have no means of swimming. They are browsed upon by the herbivorous individuals of the animal or zoo-plankton. These plant eaters, in turn, are caught and devoured by carnivorous animals. These may then be the victims of non-planktonic, predacious marine animals, like fish or squids or even some whales. We find, therefore that even in this world of diminutives there is just as well defined a food web or series of food chains as in other animal or plant communities. Basically the energy is derived from sunlight filtering through the surface waters, being converted to vegetable food by the plants and so being passed on to animal members of the plankton. It is because the energy is derived from the sun that most of the organisms are found near the surface.

We have made mention of the size of the planktonic organisms by referring to them as small. We should elaborate a little though and point out that most are small. There are, however, a large number of jellyfish which are truly planktonic and which are far from small. For instance the common orange-brown *Cyanea* jellyfish has an Arctic relative that may be 6 ft across the bell and have tentacles 18 ft long. The Portuguese man-o'-war may have tentacles up to 50 ft in length. At the other end of the scale many planktonic organisms are unicellular and no bigger than an amoeba. Indeed there are large numbers of amoeba-like creatures in the plankton which have within their microscopic bodies tiny transparent skeletons of perfect symmetry and yet they are so small

as to be invisible to the naked eye. The vast majority of planktonic organisms, though, are about the size of a water flea, or between the size of a pin-point and a pin-head. The oceans of the world teem with countless billions of these animals and plants and every swimmer must have swallowed dozens with each untimely gulp of sea water.

Perhaps one of the most intriguing facts about plankton is that many of the creatures are the minute young or larval stages of much bigger, often common, shoreline or open-water adults. In fact one vast topic within the subject of plankton is the study of these 'larval forms'. In the same way as a frog begins its life as a tadpole or a moth as a caterpillar, so a starfish begins its existence as a bipinnarian or a sea snail as a veliger. The larvae of the familiar sea-shore animals are usually small, very highly specialised, and beautifully adapted to a drifting existence. The adults are usually adapted to a sedentary or creeping existence. Because of

Pasture of the oceans: the diatoms such as these **Rhizosolenia** *and* **Guinardia** *are browsed upon by the many larval forms found in the plankton.*

DP Wilson

this extreme larval specialisation it is not surprising to find that these planktonic stages of a life cycle are completely and utterly different in appearance from the adult forms.

Unrecognisable offspring

Because the young stages look so dissimilar to their adult counterparts they were named as separate animals when they were first found and studied by biologists. The planktonic larva of the eel was called *Leptocephalus*, now it is the eel leptocephalus larva. The sea cucumber's youngster was named *Auricularia*. Now it is called the auricularian larva of a sea cucumber! The Latin names usually refer to a particular characteristic; 'auricularia' refers to an ear-like shape and 'leptocephalus' to a flat-headed appearance.

Some of the first larvae to be linked with their correct adult form were the *zoeae*

larvae and *megalopa* or second stage larvae of crabs. Barnacle larvae were also recognised early on—about 100 years ago; they start as *nauplii*, pass through six very active stages and then turn into little bivalved settling larvae which attach themselves to rocks and metamorphose or 'change their form' into barnacles as we know them on bottoms of boats and rocks. The nature of the final change is similar to that of a tadpole or caterpillar. After a time of feeding and growth and sometimes skin change, there is a sudden brief period of more rapid change and the little larva appears as a diminutive adult, often very small but unmistakably the final stage. Sometimes one is lucky enough to catch a larva in this state of change and then it is well worth studying it carefully because within half an hour a tiny starfish, or barnacle, or snail perhaps, will appear.

Why do these shoreline animals have planktonic larvae? Simply, to distribute the species far and wide. How could barnacles colonise rocks and bottoms of boats, or a permanently fixed sponge disperse, without these mobile drifting larvae?

Sometimes these youngsters tell a biologist of the affinities of the adult. A barnacle is known to be a crustacean because its nauplius larva, the tell-tale feature, is a typical crustacean larva.

Many planktonic creatures are not yet fully studied. Many larvae are not linked with adults. In Jamaica two years ago, we filmed nearly 500 species of drifting organism. There were 7 or 8 new to science and yet they were common in the waters of Kingston Bay harbour. There is still a vast wealth of knowledge to be gleaned from these tiny creatures by both professional biologists and amateurs. The creatures are easily collected in a lady's stocking, suitably held open at the top end and with a small collecting vessel tied into the toe end in which a hole has been cut. Pulled slowly through coastal waters, any day of the year, but best in summer and spring, for ten minutes or so, the net will concentrate thousands of tiny throbbing animals in the collecting tube or tin. Under a microscope these will be seen to be of the most infinite beauty and variety.

Bizarre rarities

Every now and then you may come across one of the more bizarre rarities. Some of the most fantastic species are in fact very common. One such type, a copepod, occurs in Atlantic coastal waters, a bit like a water flea, but within its body it is equipped with two incredible binocular eyes. The retina is half-way back along the body and the lens system is mounted right at the front of the head. Between retina and lens is a condenser lens and the whole system is bounded by a well-defined binocular tube. The photograph opposite shows this unusual animal which is known to prey on other species not unlike itself.

Planktonic organisms are both fundamentally essential to the vast food chains within our oceans and are also remarkably spectacular. What is more, the study of the plants and animals and their inter-relationships presents even the amateur with an open field for research.

Millions on the menu

The upper layers of the world's oceans are a vast soup of minute animals and plants: these drifting millions form the plankton. Marine life depends on them, from the immense baleen whales, which filter them direct from the water, to the predatory fish which eat them second-hand, in the bodies of their prey. (For full food chain see blue whale, p 249.)

The animal part of the plankton is mainly crustaceans (see copepod, p 518). It also serves as a drifting nursery to many larvae as they spread about the oceans (see barnacle p 145, brittlestar p 286, and hermit crab p 1056). Four larvae are shown here, and one copepod, illustrating the beauty and diversity of this all-important but unfamiliar part of the animal kingdom.

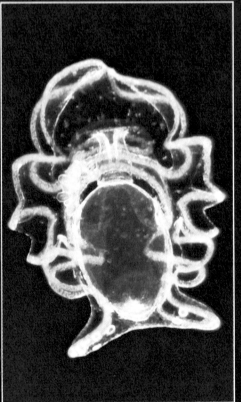

Similarities between this sea cucumber larva and that of the acorn worm (p 9) gave scientists a link between major animal groups (×150).

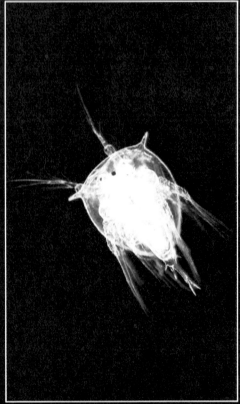

The first larval stage of a barnacle (p 145). This will swim in the plankton, moult to form a cypris, anchor, then become adult (×130).

One of the beautiful quirks of nature found in the plankton: the second (bipinnarian) stage in the development of a starfish (×70).

The coiled shell can already be seen within the star-like formation of this large veliger larva of a sea snail (×100).

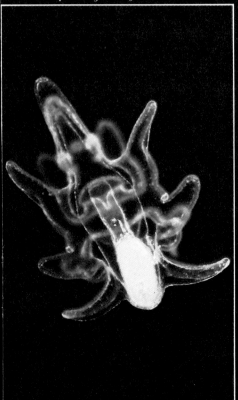

A copepod (p 518) with eyes extended to form a pair of living binoculars. The feature over-leaf explains this curious structure (×100).

Pond life

Compared with the vast amount of research that has been carried out on lakes and rivers, surprisingly little attention has been given by professional scientists to ponds; but traditionally a pond is the amateur's happy hunting ground. At a conference of zoologists in Oxford some years ago a questionnaire was passed round among those attending, asking how and when their interest in biology started. This questionnaire revealed that the majority had been avid pond hunters in their schooldays. This is not surprising for no easily available habitat provides such a generous introduction to the animal kingdom as does a pond. In quite a small one there will be examples of most of the main phyla, or divisions, of animals: many kinds of protista, or single-celled organisms including such well-known members as *Amoeba, Paramecium* and the bell animalcule *Vorticella*; sponges; coelenterates, a largely marine group (sea anemones and jellyfish) but represented in freshwater by several species of *Hydra*; flatworms; threadworms; hair worms; annelids, or segmented worms, including the leeches; bryozoans or moss animals; rotifers; arthropods, including the crustaceans, insects and water spiders; molluscs, both bivalve and univalve; and, of course, the vertebrates, represented by the fish and amphibians.

A self-contained community

The usual definition of a pond is a small body of still water shallow enough for effective light to reach the bottom so it is possible for plants to grow all the way across. Shallowness rather than surface area is important. Vegetation is essential to most pond animals; apart from providing food for the herbivorous ones, it serves as shelter and as egg-laying platforms. The release of oxygen in photosynthesis is an important means of aeration in a stagnant body of water. Finally, when the plants die and are decomposed by bacteria, the am-monium salts, phosphates and other nutrients are brought back into circulation for re-use by other organisms. A shallow, weedy pond, therefore, is a highly productive system which can support a wide diversity of animals and plants as seen in the illustration opposite.

But apart from this variety and abundance of life, pond-living animals comprise an almost self-contained community which can be readily seen and studied. It is no accident that in school biology examinations a pond takes pride of place as an exercise in ecology, and valuable contributions to research can still be made by the amateur.

Adaptations for aquatic life

Perhaps the most fascinating aspect of pond life, once the various animals have been identified, is the way in which aquatic animals are adapted to live in water. None show this better than the aquatic insects. Because they are descended from terrestrial forms that took to the water, present-day aquatic insects show an astonishing diversity of modifications to enable them to survive in an alien environment. Beetles and bugs have beautifully streamlined bodies to enable them to move quickly in the water, which must be the envy of designers of marine craft. Their speed through the water is increased by flattened oar-like legs, fringed with stiff hairs which effectively add to their width. The common whirligig beetle goes even further: its legs are formed by a system of flat plates which present a broad surface on the swimming stroke, but fold like a fan on the return stroke, with much the same effect as an oarsman 'feathering' between strokes. Dragonfly nymphs can propel themselves through the water rapidly by a form of jet propulsion.

Breathing atmospheric air might be thought a problem for land animals that have adopted water as their permanent home rather late in their evolution, but with their typical versatility aquatic insects have devised a variety of ingenious and beautiful ways of obtaining their air snorkel-like tubes for pushing just above the surface, as in the water scorpions, o air-bubble reservoirs for carrying abou below the surface. Some of these reservoir are more complex than was previousl thought, as research in recent years ha shown that some can absorb oxygen dis solved in the water and so act as a physica gill. Immature stages of insects can ofte take in oxygen through their shells, or b means of special thin-walled growths callec tracheal gills. The present purpose of som of these—as in some mayflies—seems to b as paddles for creating a current of wate to flow over the body and so bring fresl supplies of dissolved oxygen. The larva and pupae of a small group of *Donacia* beetles even tap the supply of oxygen in th air spaces of submerged water plants.

A living classroom lost?

All these exciting aspects of life in fresh water, and many more, can be studied easil by anyone who lives within reach of a smal body of water. Many schools are alread using such ponds for biology studies; anc anyone who does likewise in his own garder will have endless interest, not least in study ing the incredible ways in which a new ponc becomes colonized quite naturally anc quickly in the summer with a wide variet of life.

Unfortunately this colonisation is par of a natural process which, left unchecked will lead to the obliteration of the pond Taking advantage of the new soil createc by the decomposing remains of water plants the encroaching pondside plants reduce the open water year by year until eventuall the whole of the pond's area has been con verted to dry land. Many ponds are alsc disappearing as a result of human activities filled in with rubbish, or drained for agri cultural purposes or building. Conservatior measures such as controlled clearing o vegetation are needed to preserve thi fascinating habitat.

▷ *Animal life in a pond is arranged in zones reflecting the different conditions in and on the water.* ◁ *Schoolchildren explore a pond in Oxfordshire, England. Every pond holds a wealth of animals representing most of the major phyla from protistans to vertebrates. All one needs is a simple net and some containers for the catch, and at once a fascinating new world is within reach. Ponds are not only for children; careful research into the relationships of the animals in them can still help our knowledge of ecology.*

John Clegg

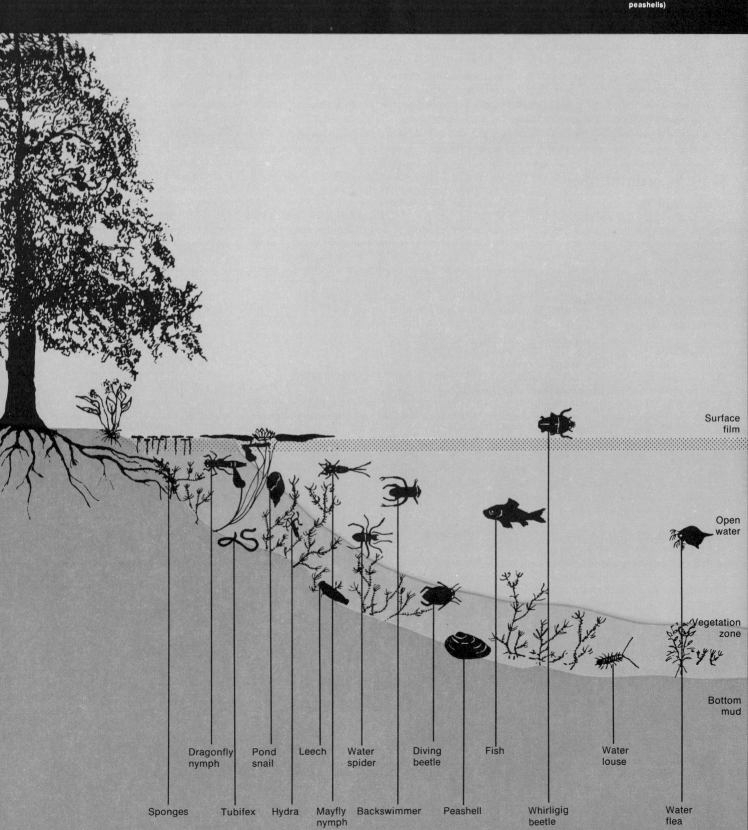

On and among water plants

Diving beetles and larvae
Backswimmers (water boatmen)
Dragonfly nymphs
Mayfly nymphs (*Cloeon*)
Water spiders
Newts (during breeding season)
Pond snails
Hydra
Sessile rotifers
Bell animals (*Vorticella*)

Under floating leaves

China mark moth caterpillars
Bryozoa (*Plumatella*)
Planarian flatworms
Small leeches

On submerged rootlets
of trees

Sponges
Moss animals

Swimming

Fish
Phantom larva, *Chaoborus*
Water fleas, *Daphnia*
Rotifers

Gnat larvae and pupae

Under the surface film

On surface

Water springtails
(primitive insects)
Pond skaters
Water measurer
Whirligig beetle

In or on the mud

Protista (*Amoeba, Paramecium*)
Nematodes (threadworms)
Segmented worms (*Tubifex*)
Crustaceans (water louse
and water flea)
Alder fly larva
Bloodworm larva of
Chironomus
Lesser water boatman, *Corixa*
Bivalve molluscs (orb- and
peashells)

Surface
film

Open
water

Vegetation
zone

Bottom
mud

Dragonfly
nymph

Pond
snail

Leech

Water
spider

Diving
beetle

Fish

Water
louse

Sponges

Tubifex

Hydra

Mayfly
nymph

Backswimmer

Peashell

Whirligig
beetle

Water
flea

Legon/Nielson

2753

Conservation

As has been shown, the animal and plant worlds are in a constant state of balance; intricate ecological webs connect the lives of every living being. Man has disturbed these webs in a variety of ways. For sport, food, or crop and game protection, he has exterminated many species of animal and brought others to the brink of extinction. In more recent years the pressure of his population, ignorant farming methods, and the indiscriminate use of cumulative toxins for pest control have combined to make the position critical for a large and ever-growing number of animals. Some, sceptics say, would have died out naturally, man or not. Yet the average rate of natural extinction is about one species every thousand years. In the last 300 years man has destroyed more than 200 forms of birds and mammals.

There is, however, another ever-increasing number of naturalists concerned with the fate of these animals, for a variety of reasons. Some just do not want to lose animals for ever; they consider them our heritage, to be passed on to future generations. Others consider the waste; with scientifically planned exploitation, many game animals could be bred instead of pushed out of their environments, and provide food for some of the starving people who are doing the pushing. Still others, more forward looking, see the world as one big habitat, reasoning that if man destroys animals and land at the present rate, he will ultimately destroy himself. This chapter is a cross-section of the conservation world. The sea-turtles represent a large source of food, if allowed to breed; pheasants are worth preserving for aesthetic reasons alone, apart from any ecological significance they may have. Pollution, in many of its ugly, world embracing forms, is described, and one unexpected conservation bonus—the nature reserve—is described. The profits from places like the Serengeti are valuable assets to depressed countries. Animals kept for profit could yet be the only survivors; conservation is still too little. It could be too late.

Man in animal life

Man creates

Man is the most paradoxical of all animals. On the one hand he is the most dangerous and destructive the world has ever known, on the other the most imaginative and creative. And he has evolved a conscience. Man's creative record is awe-inspiring—from the earliest cave paintings to Picasso, from Caxton's printing press to the Computer—but . . .

Man destroys

Man's record on the debit side is terrifying. He has destroyed much of his own creation and far too much of the natural creation. Toxic chemicals are still poisoning the world around us, although we know of the dangers. Man's greed has brought the great whales to the verge of extinction. Vast herds of antelope wandered over the plains of Africa before the advent of the 'White Hunter' and the numbers still continue to dwindle. In his destructiveness may lie the seeds of his own destruction.

The Heritage

Life, so the scientists tell us, probably began on earth something like 20 million centuries ago. The current end-products of an endless process of evolution are the plants and animals which now share the earth with mankind. They were shaped by their environment. The continents and oceans, the mountains, the plains and the forests, the great rivers, and small streams, the lakes and ponds moulded the wildlife that live in them . . .

Elephant, lion, and rhinoceros—flamingo, trout and butterfly, all the animals in this Encyclopedia are the product of their habitat. These are our heritage—the natural part of our environment—and we have a simple duty; to look after them for the generations who will follow us.

The Threat

Since the dawn of life, species have become extinct and been replaced by other evolving species, but man and his civilisation have speeded up the extinction rate by a factor of at least four. Some species are threatened today because man is killing too many, but most (both animals and plants) are in danger because their habitat is being destroyed, often thoughtlessly and unnecessarily, because not enough people understand or care. Man cuts down the forests, drains the marshes, and pollutes the rivers, the sea, the atmosphere and the soil. When the web of interrelationship between plants and animals is broken, when human beings change the habitat in which they were evolved too quickly for them to adapt to the new conditions, they can only die out. This then is the threat and it is present-day man who will stand condemned unless he can prevent it.

The four pillars of conservation
Ethical

Whether or not right and wrong exist outside the context of human social progress, man is acutely aware of the distinction between good and evil. In his heart of hearts he knows that it is wrong to cause the extinction of other animals. He easily recognises a moral duty to conserve the living renewable resources of the earth and to pass them on intact to succeeding generations.

Aesthetic

Nature can evoke deep feelings in the human heart and can recall from the distant past, man's true roots; wildlife and wilderness can give spiritual refreshment and recreation. Money is freely and willingly given for education; to buy pictures and build cathedrals. Conserving wildlife falls into the same class. To maintain the treasures in the British Museum is desirable; so it is to preserve Exmoor, the Serengeti plains and the Yellowstone Park. These are places of beauty which give pleasure to mankind. It is no less vandalism to destroy the works of nature than to destroy the achievements of man.

Scientific

Man's own survival depends not only on his capacity to deal with the thermonuclear explosion and the population explosion but also on his capacity to stop carelessly plundering the planet. He must learn to apply the science of ecology to himself so that he can learn, before it is too late, that he is a part of the intricate relationship between all living things. Nature is a vast treasure-house of knowledge, but, as this Wildlife Encyclopedia shows, it is as yet hardly explored. Wildlife (which in its widest context includes anything alive and wild—animal or plant) is the raw material of biological science but some species are becoming extinct before they can be properly studied.

Economic

Wildlife is a valuable asset as a renewable natural resource, particularly in developing countries, and can contribute to the economy, especially through tourism. Already, in some countries of Africa, for example, tourism may soon become the leading industry and is an important source of overseas currency. People come from all over the world to see and photograph wildlife. If the animals vanished, many of the tourists would stay away. Wildlife, if intelligently managed and husbanded, can also be a valuable source of much needed protein.

What must be done

When there is an unavoidable collision between the survival of man and the survival of wildlife, human interest is likely to prevail. But such collisions are rare and in most cases a little thought, ingenuity and goodwill permits co-existence of man and wildlife. We must first learn to recognise that these dangers exist and that we ourselves shall be the losers if we do nothing about it. We must make sure that everyone everywhere understands the threat, accepts the responsibility and appreciates that it is in the mainstream of human progress to avert it. What is needed now are more and larger areas set aside for wildlife-reserves, more sanctuaries and National Parks; more conservation legislation—better laws and better law enforcement; more conservation research to find out exactly why species and habitats are threatened and exactly how to save them; more programmes for breeding threatened animals in captivity so they can be returned to their natural habitats; more conservation education and campaigns to make the world aware of the existing problem and to avert specific disasters; and most important of all . . . more money for these various activities which will help to save the world's wildlife and wild places.

The Editors are grateful to the World Wildlife Fund for help with this article.

The unnecessary slaughter of the world's beautiful and interesting wild animals is brought home by two pictures from Africa. Above: leopard and cheetah trophies for the East African souvenir trade. Below: a police officer with a collection of rhino horns confiscated from poachers.

Pollution and animal life

The last 25 years have seen a revolution in the use of chemicals by the farmer. New synthetic products, starting with DDT, have played a key part in increasing food production and relatively few of these are dangerous to animal life. Modern herbicides, for example, are mostly harmless, though they may have important indirect effects by changing the environment. Pesticides, by contrast, are designed to kill animal life, usually insects, and they are rarely selective. At first the new synthetic pesticides seemed to offer a 'miracle' control, but now many economic entomologists are realising the dangers of such a blanket attack whilst there has been a growing appreciation of the threat, often insidious, some pose to wild life and perhaps, if unrestricted, even to human beings.

Deadly and persistent

Two groups of synthetic pesticides have caused the most concern. The organophosphorus compounds, discovered as a by-product of wartime research on nerve gases, can be fiercely toxic. One, parathion, has killed many human beings, accidentally or sometimes as a suicide agent. In Holland it caused the deaths of some 200 000 birds of 55 species in 1960. These pesticides, however, soon lose their toxicity and much less deadly varieties have come into use. More serious are the organochlorines (such as DDT and its more potent successors endrin, aldrin and dieldrin). They are highly stable and persistent—valuable qualities in an insecticide—but this means that they may contaminate the environment for years,

perhaps far from the site of their original use. Thus DDT used in Canada to spray spruce forests drained into the Miramichi river, killing all the young salmon; more recently 10 million fish died at the mouth of the Mississippi, killed by chemicals, especially aldrin and dieldrin, applied hundreds of miles away.

Moreover, the organochlorines can pass, almost unchanged, from one organism in the food chain to another. So DDT sprayed on Dutch elms in the USA passed into the dead leaves and then to earthworms, which killed the birds feeding on them. Dieldrin, used in sheep-dips, may pass into the flesh of the sheep and so to golden eagles, or human beings. Sometimes the concentration of poison increases markedly during this process. At Clear Lake, California, DDT applied at one-fiftieth of a part per million (ppm) to kill gnats, reached 5 ppm in plankton, up to 300 ppm in fish and 1 600 ppm in the fat of their predators, the western grebes. The grebe population fell from over 1 000 pairs to 30 pairs by 1960—and none of these reared young.

Immediate action needed

Organochlorines can also kill directly, as in eastern England in 1960 and 1961 when thousands of birds died after feeding on dressed seeds. Restrictions on their use rapidly ended this mass slaughter and since then the main sufferers in Britain have been the predatory birds at the end of food chains. Peregrine numbers, for example, had fallen by 1962 to one-half the pre-war level and only a quarter of the remnant were nesting successfully. Golden eagles in western Scotland suffered a catastrophic decline in fertility. The persistent

organochlorines can act insidiously. Stored readily in the fat, they can be harmful even in apparently healthy birds, for they may be harmful to the offspring, or to the adult at times of stress, such as migration. The eggs may be infertile, the young weakly, or, as has recently been shown, their interference with the calcium-producing mechanisms may cause the egg-shells to be too thin. Peregrines have become extinct in the eastern USA, where, also, the osprey and the American national bird, the bald eagle, have shown a drop in fertility and the same trend to thinner eggshells.

Many of the developed countries of the world, alarmed by the effects of the organochlorines—the growth of resistant strains among insect pests, the rise of new pests when their natural predators have been destroyed, the effects on wild life and the rise of residue levels in human food—are now imposing some restrictions. Sweden has banned a different chemical, methylmercury. Many countries have recently banned or restricted the use of organochlorines. Yet migrant birds may pick up poisons in their winter quarters in Africa or Asia, and, equally important, the winds and waters spread such persistent pollution widely. Lakes in the barrens of north Canada are affected, perhaps by spray droplets windborne for hundreds of miles, and DDT residues have been found in fish far out in the Pacific and in Adélie penguins and crabeater seals which spend their entire lives in the Antarctic. Ignorance of the subtle and far-reaching ecological effects of some pesticides may excuse their sledgehammer use in the past; we now know enough to realise that controls on such chemicals must be worldwide.

On land, in the air and on water, pollution by modern chemicals is a threat to wildlife, some chemicals persisting and getting into our own food. Their cumulative effect in our own bodies is not yet known.

J Allan Cash

Shell Photo

Conservation and breeding of rare pheasants

With the exception of waterfowl, no family of birds lends itself more readily to conservation in captivity than the pheasant family. There is a good reason for this. In the wild a female pheasant will lay one clutch of eggs, which may vary in number from 4 or 5 eggs up to 12 or 14. She will then go broody and hatch these, and the number hatched and reared will vary from perhaps one or two up to about 10. In contrast, in a spacious aviary a hen pheasant will continue to lay for a considerable period if the eggs are collected daily, and as many as 30 eggs may be laid by one hen as she will not usually go broody under this system. Even if she does start to sit the nest can be destroyed by the aviary attendant, and one or more further clutches will usually be layed.

Most breeders of pheasants adopt this procedure of collecting the eggs every day and then hatching them by using bantams or small fowls as foster mothers. A strain of bantams that will hatch and rear the young pheasants is easily built up, and is a vital part of every pheasant breeder's equipment. Taking into account the ease with which pheasants in captivity can be fed nowadays, by using the proprietary pellets produced for feeding turkeys, it will be seen that with care and attention to detail some very worthwhile results can be obtained.

The future of pheasants in the wild, however, presents a much gloomier picture. In most parts of Asia, where the pheasants are found wild, the local human populations have a low subsistence level, and a pheasant is a very desirable meal. Also it is easy to stoot or trap, and thus a rapidly increasing human population can soon rid an area of its pheasants.

With the exception of the genus *Phasianus*, the true or game pheasants, the natural habitat of pheasants is forest, but natural forests are being reduced at an alarming rate. In such a situation aviculture provides the only hope of saving a species from extinction as it is obviously useless to re-introduce pheasants to areas where they have become very rare if the habitat itself is threatened. If it is not, and re-introduction is proposed, other causes of decline must be looked for and of course remedied before new stock is turned loose.

Sometimes it is possible to introduce a species to a new area, but in this case great care must be taken before it is done, as rare endemic plants or insects might themselves be threatened by an alien species of bird, or other related birds could be endangered by a disease or parasite not previously found in the locality arriving in or on the bodies of the introduced pheasants.

A captive majority

At the present time a situation exists in which there are several species of pheasants which are more plentiful in aviaries than they are in the wild. The best example of this is the golden pheasant *Chrysolophus pictus* which is a common bird in aviaries throughout the civilised world. This species well illustrates the important point that the best chances of success in conservation in captivity are with those species that are exceptionally beautiful and will therefore be kept by a large number of people. Any breeder can obtain unrelated birds to mate with his own stock and thus combat the effects of inbreeding. It is well known that inbreeding rapidly leads to infertility, bad hatchability, and eventually complete sterility. That close relative of the golden pheasant, the Lady Amherst pheasant *Chrysolophus amherstiae*, is also well established in captivity, but unfortunately some strains are not pure as crossing has taken place with the golden pheasant in the past.

When an attempt is to be made to establish a species of pheasant in captivity it is important in the first instance to start with as many individuals as possible, otherwise inbreeding depression will be evident very soon, and all efforts are then wasted. If only a few pairs are available, then as many as possible should be bred as quickly as possible, so that after a few generations some distantly related birds are available, as opposed to brothers and sisters or cousins, and these will be nearly as useful as unrelated specimens. When the number of individuals of a species in captivity reaches 100 or more it should be possible, in theory at least, to combat all the ill effects of inbreeding.

With certain genera of pheasants such as the tragopans, which are greatly endangered, setbacks are frequent, mainly because the hens lay few eggs compared with more prolific species. They lay usually less than 15 a year. This makes it difficult to build up a large stock rapidly enough to combat inbreeding depression. A good example of this in reverse is the case of Hume's bar-tailed pheasant, *Syrmaticus humiae*, which had never been seen in the western world until imported to Stagsden Bird Gardens in Bedfordshire, England in 1961. Four pairs were imported and large stocks were rapidly built up as they are prolific layers. It is now well established in Britain and there are also large stocks in Europe and America.

Pheasants in danger

It is only in the last 10 or 15 years that conservationists have come to realise how greatly pheasants as a group are in need of protection. It is not possible to find out the actual status of many species. Temminck's tragopan, *Tragopan temmincki*, the eared pheasants, *Crossoptilon* spp. and the several races of the blood pheasants, *Ithaginis cruentus*, occur in countries such as China and Nepal, which are not easily accessible because of political boundaries or high mountainous terrain. For instance, it has only recently been discovered that the cheer pheasant, *Catreus wallichi*, which lives wild only in the small area of the Himalayas in the extreme north of West Pakistan, is in grave danger of extinction. Fortunately there is a small stock in captivity in most countries of the western world.

Looking 50 years ahead it seems inevitable that many pheasants will in fact be extinct in the wild, but equally reasonable to suppose that their beauty will be enjoyed by a great many people who will see them in bird collections and zoos throughout the world. If this is so, then the efforts of present and future breeders will have been more than worthwhile.

▽ *Magnificent metallic sheen identifies the male Himalayan monal. It is hard to say how many survive in the Himalayas, but numbers are decreasing.*

▽ *Resplendent male satyr tragopan. Tragopans are more at home in trees than other pheasants and will often nest in abandoned nests as high as 40 ft.*

Fred Johnson

Sea turtle conservation

The conservation of sea turtles, which are found throughout tropical and subtropical seas, poses special problems involving international agreements. There are many economic and scientific reasons for promoting their conservation.

The best-known of the seven species of turtle is the green turtle *Chelonia mydas,* from which turtle soup is made. It may be more than 4 ft long over the shell and weigh 300–400 lb. The largest turtle is the luth or leathery turtle *Dermochelys coriacea* with a shell length of up to 8 ft and a weight of over half a ton. The other species are the hawksbill *Eretmochelys imbricata,* whose carapace shields provide tortoiseshell, the loggerhead *Caretta caretta,* the two species of ridleys, *Lepidochelys kempi* and *L. olivacea,* and the flatback *Chelonia depressa,* the least known of the world's sea turtles.

Most species of sea turtles are now rare and threatened with extinction in large areas of their range. It is interesting to investigate why they have become scarce.

Linked to the land

Sea turtles evolved from land-dwelling reptiles which laid eggs and they have retained this one vital link with life on land. The female turtles come ashore to dig a nest on a sandy beach above the high tide mark. During incubation many nests are destroyed by predators (mainly mammals and monitor lizards) and the hatchling turtles are heavily preyed upon as they enter the sea. Many are lost to predators as they grow, but with each year's growth they have fewer enemies, until, when they are adults, only very large sharks can eat them. Only one in a thousand baby turtles entering the sea will survive to breeding age. Although this seems a very high level of mortality, the long life and rate of egg laying must be considered. Once breeding age is reached after 4 years or more, depending on the species, several clutches of eggs are laid in a nesting season. The green turtle, which nests only about every third year, lays a clutch of eggs every 15 days throughout the summer. When the average clutch of 110 eggs is multiplied by 6 or 8, the egg production per female is impressive. Furthermore, each adult female probably survives to breed a number of times. In order to maintain their numbers, each pair of adult turtles has to produce only two others surviving to adulthood to replace them. Viewed in this way, turtles do not seem threatened. Nor would they be but for the demands of modern man.

Too tasty a dish

Turtles have been eaten by coastal peoples for many thousands of years. It was the colonisation of America by Europeans, however, which began the spectacular decline in turtle numbers there and led to the first protective legislation which was passed in Bermuda in the early 17th century. Since then turtles have been slaughtered in their thousands in many parts of the world for export to European cities, and more recently the United States, to make the famous turtle soup served at banquets round the world.

As we have seen turtles are adapted to withstand the very high mortality rate among their young, but man takes the adults, especially the breeding females, which are easy prey as they are slow and clumsy on land. In many parts of the world the females are killed before they have laid their eggs which means that three years' egg production is lost.

To the demand for turtle soup can now be added the demand for their meat, both for native and tourist consumption, and for their leather, which has recently become

▽ *The flatback turtle is a rarity. It is found only in northern Australian waters.*

▽ *Eggs by the dozen: a female green turtle lays about 9 dozen eggs at a time.*

▽ *Baby green turtles head for the sea. Only one in every thousand reaches adulthood.*

▽ *This simple inexpensive hatchery in Queensland holds up to 50 000 eggs.*

Photos by HR Bustard

very fashionable. In 1967, for instance, 336 *tons* of ridley turtle skins were taken in Mexican waters alone. The eggs, too, are taken for food, and on some beaches people collect every clutch. Operations of this kind will clearly result in the rapid extermination of turtles in these localities. Young turtles are taken for their shells or to be stuffed whole for sale to tourists.

Proposed courses of action

A secure future for the world's sea turtles depends on two main lines of research. The first of these is a thorough study of the population biology of the species in order to state precisely when a population is being overexploited and what level of egg consumption and annual take of large turtles is permissible without driving them into extinction. When this is done, governments will probably be more likely to protect the turtle populations as they will then have statistics on which to base their control figures and a profitable resource can be easily recognised. As well as being an important source of protein, so badly needed in much of the tropics, the calipee is used to make soup and the skins in particular are a valuable cash crop. In many parts of the world, however, the migratory habits of the turtles make effective conservation a very difficult task, as international agreements, which are extremely difficult to achieve, are needed.

The other alternative is to devise a scheme whereby turtles can be regularly bred in captivity. Certainly it is possible to rear baby turtles commercially in captivity, although little large-scale work has been attempted. The damage in commercial turtle ranching is that it will merely increase the demand for eggs, posing a further threat to the species, so it is essential to encourage them to breed in captivity. Once this is achieved 'battery turtles' can safely be produced, which would help to reduce the pressure on the wild populations.

The extremely localised nesting beaches are used by large turtle populations, so it is especially important to preserve them. In developed countries many rookeries have been disturbed or ruined completely by wasted developments. It is essential for the main breeding areas to be set aside as national parks.

After five years of sea turtle research on the Great Barrier Reef of Australia by experts the Queensland Government has extended complete protection to all species of sea turtles and their eggs throughout the State of Queensland in Queensland waters. The coastline of Queensland covers 3 200 miles and the Barrier Reef 1 250 miles, so this legislation protects the large sea turtle populations of the six species which occur there. This legislation has provided a huge natural study area where research can be carried out to help conserve populations elsewhere. There are now plans to set up other national parks for sea turtles in Queensland; already the cabinet has approved a national park specifically for the protection of the flatback turtle.

If sea turtles enjoy total effective protection by law, combined with national parks to protect their habitats (in this case nesting beaches) then their future is assured.

Serengeti today

If we had been born a few hundred years ago, we would have found the great prairies of North America supporting vast numbers of bison; Europe too has had its large herds, and the African plains carried uncountable quantities of game. Today, we have so altered our surroundings that many people can spend their lives without ever seeing a large wild animal. But there are still a few places left where you can see these great herds as they used to occur — in Africa you must go to the Serengeti.

In East Africa, just south of the equator, the Serengeti stretches for 5 000 square miles of bushland and plains. Here you can drive across the open grasslands and pass through a million gazelle and half a million wildebeest and zebra. It is the largest single collection of such animals left anywhere in the world. These great herds of wildebeest and zebra are continually moving, as they must have a constant supply of fresh drinking water, and during the dry season they can find this only in the permanent rivers in the bushland to the north and west of the park. The plains in the east contain several small lakes, but these are harsh alkaline waters formed by the endless evaporation and concentration of the salts washed from the volcanic soils. Flocks of flamingoes feed there, but the game animals cannot drink.

When the rains arrive, the tender grasses out on the plains grow lush and green and small pools develop in the hollows. The animals can now move out onto the grasslands, where they wander constantly, grazing at the short grass and then passing on to let it grow again, before returning to graze again. This regular movement and migration of such large herds dominates the life of many of the other animals, especially predators and scavengers.

Not as stable as it seems

But the Serengeti is not an ancient monument that can be left and admired. No national park today can be considered as a complete, self-contained unit, and even the vast Serengeti is not large enough to be self-supporting. Animals continue to move across its boundaries to spend part of their year outside the park, and these areas must be safeguarded by restrictions on shooting and cultivation. Although man's destructive influence within the park may be minimal, the activities outside the boundaries may greatly influence it. Until about 15 years ago, elephants were never found within the park. But since 1955 there has been a slow invasion, until today there are some 2 000 elephants in the Serengeti. Both cultivation and shooting in the areas to the north have probably driven them into the protection of the park. Such a large-scale immigration could greatly affect the area, and indeed in some places the animals have not been able to find their normal food plants and have started knocking down the larger trees to feed off the branches.

The long-term effects of 'tree-eating elephants' are extremely important to the other animals — trees not only provide food, but they also give shade and affect the soil and grasses growing nearby. In order to manage the park efficiently we must have carefully planned research work to find out the effects of these types of problems and to try and solve them.

Three years ago the Serengeti Research Institute was established to undertake this basic ecological research, with the express aim of developing a guided management policy for the national park. Only when we understand how these great animal populations are regulated will we be able to conserve this unique animal community.

Plant research needed

One of the essential priorities is to understand how the different plant communities are developed and maintained — for ultimately all the animals depend on the plants for their food. Every year in the dry season, grassland fires sweep across the park. In order for any young trees to survive in an area, there must be at least two or three years with no burnings, to enable the plants to grow large enough to survive the flames. At the present rate of burning this means that there is very little regeneration taking place, and in some areas those trees which are dying or being killed by the invading elephants might never be replaced. The large *Acacia tortilis* trees are probably the most important species in the park and almost all these trees are from 40 to 60 years old. This corresponds to a time at the turn of the century when a massive outbreak of the disease rindepest, which is fatal to domestic cattle, caused the Masai tribesmen to desert the area for many years. The resulting lack of camp fires may have meant that there were considerably fewer grassland fires and many seedlings might have developed during this convenient pause in the burning. Since then, few young trees have been able to survive.

At present, if we are to ensure that the woodlands are not to disappear forever, we must allow some young trees to grow by preventing the fires. To do this we must build firebreaks, or deliberately start fires early in the season, so the resulting fire will be comparatively cool and may not damage the young trees. Incidentally, the prevention of fires will also lead to a thicker growth of small shrubs and bushes which may provide the elephants with additional food and solve the problem of tree damage.

The overall picture

Slowly the picture will be pieced together as each animal is studied in turn. Why do the wildebeest numbers fluctuate so greatly? Do predators control the size of the game herds? How important a factor is disease in a wild animal community? Only when we know the answer to these types of questions will we be able to take the right action to maintain this unique community. We can no longer afford to 'leave it to nature'.

Of course, research must be backing a well managed park. Poaching must continually be kept in check, new roads built and new hotels opened. Last year over 17 000 people came to see the Serengeti. With new hotels being built, even more people will be able to come and enjoy this piece of unspoilt Africa. In a rapidly changing world we must ensure that everything possible is done to safeguard the Serengeti.

▽ *During the dry season herds of zebra may have to travel over 100 miles in search of fresh water.*

▽ *Wildebeeste and zebra roam the grassy plains.*

Photos by David Houston

Man and animals

Man has always had close associations with animals. Primarily they served as a source of food; but as man's social structure and system of communication developed his attitude changed and animals began to figure prominently in his art, myth and legend. Although the mythical aspect of animals is fast disappearing today, for past cultures animals symbolised the very forces of life. Much of man's fear and reverence of animals stemmed from religious belief or underlying envy of their physical prowess. Egyptian gods were usually represented in animal form; the ibis was held sacred together with the dog and scarab beetle—the cow is still held sacred by the Hindus in India. The eagle and the bull, strong and aggressive animals, have always represented powerful forces, similarly the snake and the dove represent evil and peace respectively.

The belief that man could change into animal form, lycanthropy, figured prominently in the lives of European people during the Dark Ages. People were terrified to walk in woods at night for fear of meeting a creature such as a werewolf, half man half beast, that was especially fond of human flesh.

Domestication and exploitation are nearly synonymous; a neglected aspect of man-animal relationship is the use of animals in war. For centuries the horse has been used by man to gain mobility in territorial disputes and dogs and pigeons have acted as messengers.

Throughout history, while the majority of people were content with fanciful and fantastic ideas about animals, there were others who took a more realistic approach. Early scientists gradually built up a logical picture of the animal world. In the Encyclopedia we deal with Audubon who devoted most of his time to drawing and writing about the wildlife of North America.

John James Laforet Audubon (1785-1851)

Mary Evans

Audubon was born in the State of Louisiana, but spent his childhood and early youth in France. His father was a prosperous and adventurous man, an officer in the French navy with business connections and property in America. He was away from France for long periods of time, leaving the young Audubon in the care of his second wife. She spoiled her stepson, letting him wander around the countryside, which he preferred above all other pastimes. He used to go out collecting birds' eggs, lichens and flowers, turning his small bedroom into a fascinating museum of natural objects all tastefully arranged and displayed. At the age of 16 he started on a series of 200 drawings of the birds of France. He was a little disappointed with them, but he was determined to persevere and improve on them.

In the early half of the 19th century, France was a powerful country, and many young men were recruited for the army. Audubon's father was anxious for his son's safety and was sure that if he sent him to America he would have a much freer life. So, at the age of 17 Audubon returned to his native country. His home for many years was at Mill Grove Farm in a beautiful wooded part of Pennsylvania. Here he was well looked after by a quaker and his family. These were happy days for Audubon, who spent most of his time hunting, fishing and drawing the great variety of wildlife of the region. One of his favourite pastimes was to go down to the creek, where a pair of phoebes built their nest every year. He watched their behaviour closely, making pencil sketches of their dashing flight as they chased insects over the water. He soon made many friends and was well thought of, but considered a little eccentric as he used to go out hunting in breeches, with silk stockings and the finest ruffled shirts.

While at Mill Grove he met the girl he was to marry, Lucy Bakewell, the daughter of an Englishman. She accompanied Audubon around America and on his later visit to Europe.

After the marriage they moved south to Kentucky. This was the first of many moves. Indeed, the pattern of Audubon's life was one of constant change and only a brief synopsis can be given. Audubon was a very enthusiastic and likeable man but he had little business sense. His father had given him many contacts who initially helped him with business ventures, but unfortunately many of these failed. Audubon preferred to paint and draw the birds and animals he loved. After some time he had to take almost any job he could find, to support his wife and growing family. He worked in a museum, drew portraits, and even gave dancing lessons. In the meantime he had amassed a large folio of drawings and in 1824, encouraged by friends, he set off for Philadelphia in the hope of getting his bird paintings published. The trip was a failure, due to rivalry with George Ord, another naturalist, who considered many of Audubon's drawings inaccurate and objected to the incorporation of plants in the pictures.

His journey north was not, however, a complete waste of time as he met the chairman of the Lyceum of Natural History in New York, to whom he showed his drawings. He also delivered a lecture to the society from two papers he made on the study of swallows. After years of observation on these birds, he noted that they migrated and did not hibernate in caves or in the mud of ponds, as was popularly supposed. He returned to Louisiana and decided that he would have more chance of having his book *The Birds of America* published in Europe. In 1830 he went to England. Things improved for him there; he met many notable naturalists who found his work both attractive and scientifically correct. Colour plates were made of his *Birds* in Edinburgh. He also sold many drawings and sketches and with this money he planned expeditions for more specimens.

On his return, the first journey planned was to Labrador with his sons Victor and John. They set off in their schooner in early summer, but sailed into bad weather as they went north; they encountered violent hurricanes and dense fogs, and Audubon found the mosquitoes intolerable. Nevertheless, he and his sons collected numerous birds, plants and animals. A highlight of the voyage was when they approached the famous Bird Rock. It appeared to be covered with snow, but as they drew nearer the snow was in fact thousands of gannets nesting close together on the rock ledges. Audubon made over 20 drawings, additions to his *The Birds of America,* including drawings of razorbills and the beautiful great northern diver. His next journey was four years later, to the swamplands of Texas and Louisiana where, apart from his studies, he took his friend Edward Harris on an alligator hunt.

Between travels he worked on the text for his great bird book, the *Ornithological Biography,* later published in five large volumes. After this he started on *The Quadrupeds of North America* but did not live to see this work completed. At the age of 59, he planned a further expedition to the upper Missouri and Yellowstone country; this was to be the last of the 'grand tours'. While travelling he kept an extensive diary of his experiences and the animals he encountered. In South Dakota he remarked how different the song of the meadowlark was to that of the one found further east. This proved to be the first account of the western meadowlark. He also discovered many other small birds, which he named after his friends, and he collected more material for *The Quadrupeds* and for his third great book, *The Viviparous Quadrupeds of North America.*

Audubon loved the outdoor life; he once remarked: '. . . I wonder that men can consent to swelter and fret their lives away, amid those hot bricks and pestilent vapours, when the woods and fields are all so near'. He was fortunate that as he grew older his sons took over the task of completing many of the paintings that he was unable to finish due to his failing eyesight. The last years of his life were spent on his estate of 'Minnies Land' overlooking the Hudson river.

Animals in magic

Every year an increasing number of British tourists spend their holidays in Spain and the one event which continues to attract them is the *corrida* or bullfight. The English, renowned for their sense of 'fair play' and devotion to animals, are, more often than not, horrified by this spectacle of ritual slaughter, and many people fail to understand how the Spaniard can derive pleasure from this life and death drama, where the tremendous physical presence of the bull is as much an object of veneration as the skill of the matador.

The admiration for the bull in the modern *corrida* is more easily comprehensible when we consider the extent to which animals of all species were revered by our early ancestors. Indeed primitive man believed that other animals could speak, think and reason as well as himself, and he noted that certain animals displayed powers far superior to his own. It was only natural, therefore, that he should want to obtain some of these qualities for himself—in the case of the bull, his vigorous sexual potency and overwhelming strength. To this end the Minoans of Ancient Crete performed a magic ceremony, known as bull-leaping, in which athletes would grasp the bull by the horns as it charged and somersault onto its back. They believed that the bull's fertile power was concentrated in the horns and that by touching them the athlete would be impregnated with some of the bull's characteristics. A similar ceremony persists in the Portuguese bullfight in which the bull is not slaughtered but is pulled to the ground by its horns.

Similarly other primitive peoples hoped to acquire extraordinary qualities by eating the flesh of particular animals. To eat the lion would mean that you had absorbed his courage; to eat a hare would make you into a coward. Because the bear is a hairy creature, it was thought that baldness could be cured by rubbing bear's grease on the head.

Well-documented totems

The ancient Egyptians, however, have provided us with the most informative examples of animal worship. From the numerous papyri still preserved and from details of archaeological discoveries, we can see that the Egyptians imagined their gods either in animal form or with a human body and the head of an animal. The goddess of the sky, Hathor, was thought of in terms of a cow and the god associated with the dead, Anubis, was depicted as a dog or jackal. Not all the gods, however, were so instantly recognizable from their animal form. Pregnant women sought help from the goddess Taurt, who was seen as having the head partly of a crocodile and partly of a hippopotamus, a back resembling a crocodile, human breasts and feet like those of a lion.

These animals, because of their links with the divine, were held to be sacred and were treated with all the ceremony and devotion traditionally accorded to the god. Cats were particularly venerated at Bubastis, the cult centre of the cat-goddess Bast, and anyone who killed a cat was immediately punished with death. If a cat died a natural death, it was customary for the members of the

A sacred cockerel plays a magical part in this Ashanti fortune-telling device from Africa. The outcome of throwing the balls into the dish decides whether the omens are good or bad.

 Axel Poignant

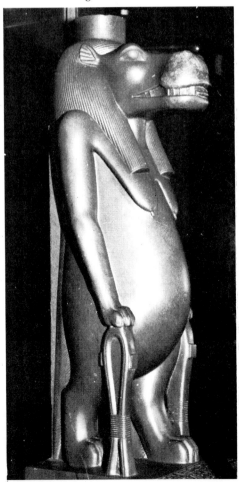

△ *Mexico: a squat terror of the underworld; one of the guardians of the earth.*
▽ *Africa: part crocodile, hippopotamus, lion and human — the goddess Taurt.*

household to shave off their eyebrows. Crocodiles, the incarnation of the crocodile-god Sebek, were kept in a special pool and were fed regular meals of bread, flesh and wine. Elsewhere they were adorned with jewels and bracelets.

In the case of the bull only one animal, distinguished by certain markings, was regarded as the incarnation of the deity. Once the Apis bull, as it was known, had been selected, it was transported in a barge lined with gold to its cult centre at Memphis. Here it lived in sumptuous surroundings, receiving the most delicate and expensive food and water from a special well, because the waters of the Nile were thought to be too fattening.

Worship of the extraordinary

In other parts of the world individual animals became objects of worship because they possessed certain characteristics which distinguished them from the rank and file of their species. In Siam, for instance, the white or albino elephant was so sacred that even the king was not permitted to climb on

△ *North America: Red Indian woodcarving wears an animal skin for protection.*

its back. These animals were so well cared for that many of them died prematurely of indigestion. When a young albino elephant calf was caught, it was put into the hands of a human nurse who reared it at her breast. If it fell sick, the most celebrated doctor in the land was summoned.

Animals have also been associated with the Devil and the bizarre worship of dark forces. Great numbers of domestic pets, including cats, dogs, owls and toads, were burnt with their owners during the witchcraft mania which swept Europe in the 16th century. Witches were traditionally believed to have 'familiars', spirits in the form of domestic animals, who would assist them in their evil practices. The life of the 'familiar' was inextricably linked with that of the witch and any wound the animal received would also be reflected on the body of the witch.

Today these strange customs and beliefs have for the most part disappeared, although traces of the supernatural powers once attributed to animals are still to be found in folktales and local superstition.

△ *Egypt, about 1100 BC: the ibis-headed Thoth, god of magic, wisdom and learning.*
▽ *Assyria, 885 BC: eagle-headed genie — a kind of under-god — sprinkling sacred water.*

Lycanthropy

The belief that men could change themselves, under certain circumstances, into animal form, has been prevalent from earliest times. The Romans took it for granted that werewolves roamed the dark forests of Germany. Virgil claimed that the transformation from man to beast was due to drugs, and his theory persisted into medieval times. Even today in such places as Transylvania, on the wooded plateau land of the Carpathian Mountains, the peasants cross themselves nervously when travelling abroad at night, believing that the dismal woods from which the area takes its name are the haunt of men-wolves, ever eager to devour human flesh.

Readers of Bram Stoker's famous horror story 'Dracula' will remember that the evil Count's castle was situated in Transylvania. Although the word 'lycanthropy' strictly speaking refers only to werewolves, the term has become synonymous with any form of man-beast transformation, whether the human-animal be blood-sucking bat—as in Count Dracula's case—wolf, tiger, or lion.

The lycanthropic myth is widespread. In Scandinavia, men become bears; in Europe, wolves; in Asia and Africa, lions, tigers, leopards or hyaenas, and in South America, bats and jaguars. The transformation traditionally takes place either through drug taking—as in Virgil's theory—or through enchantment or deliberate effort on the part of the man concerned. RL Stevenson's story of 'Doctor Jekyll and Mr Hyde' has overtones of both drug-taking and the conscious desire to become a beast.

In Britain and Scandinavia lycanthropy came into its own during the Dark Ages, at the times of the Viking raids. It frequently accompanied periods of outlawry—the ber-serkers wore bear- or wolf-skin garments and were subject to paroxysms of bestial fury, a pathological condition which may account for later outbreaks of cattle maiming in England—'madmen' tore at throats of cattle with their teeth and nails.

Later, during the great witch trials, the unfortunate old women involved were often accused of possessing the power to become animal at will—although generally speaking they took the relatively harmless forms of cats and toads. In the early 17th century, a Scottish witch, Isobel Gowdie, confessed that she often changed herself into a hare in order to travel to her witches' sabbats in secrecy. The devil, in the Middle Ages, was usually envisaged as a goat, and many coven leaders—usually male—were accused of either dressing as a goat or actually taking on goat form by supernatural means.

Werewolves of Europe

But it was on the Continent, rather than in Britain, that lycanthropy was most feared. An old folk tale common to Germany, France, and Scandinavia tells how a woodman, travelling home late at night, was attacked by a huge grey wolf. Fortunately, he was carrying his felling-axe with him, and managed to drive off the animal, hacking off its left fore-paw in the process. Arriving home, he was horrified to find his wife sitting in front of the fire and nursing the bleeding stump of her left wrist!

In France, werewolves were known as 'loups-garous' and were amazingly common in the 16th century. Oddly enough those captured and brought to trial suffered less than witches—who were feared in a similar way. Witches were burned alive; but loups-garous were generally convicted as being criminally insane. One of the last, and most famous of the 'loups-garous' was Francois Bertrand, 25-year-old sergeant in the French Army. In 1847, Bertrand was tried, and sentenced to one year's imprisonment, for lycanthropy. Fortunately, Bertrand attacked only the dead, but his twenty-page confession makes terrible reading. In his statement the sergeant confessed to having 'furiously bestial attacks' during which he would visit graveyards, dig up newly buried corpses, and rend them with his teeth.

One of the most recent outbreaks of men taking animal form received publicity in the early 1950's, during the Mau-Mau terrorism in Kenya. Many of the Mau-Mau were merely orthodox guerrilla fighters, armed with modern weapons and equipment, but others, probably independent of the organised forces, were leopard-men. Whether or not these 'leopard-men', or their counterparts in other areas of Africa, actually believed that they had taken on the form of the animal they impersonated, body and soul, is a moot point.

Today the idea of lycanthropy is dying out in all but the most backward countries. Lycanthropy would nowadays be described as 'a pathological condition betraying itself in bestial behaviour', and certainly such cases are common enough. Exactly why men believed so widely in werewolves and their ilk is still a subject of controversy. The many examples of 'wild' children apparently raised by animals—as in the Romulus and Remus story—may have helped to spread the myth, and totemism in various forms doubtless contributed to the existing legends. Perhaps the widespread fear and admiration of mankind for mighty, carnivorous animals was the most powerful factor involved; mankind, having matured and lost most of his more primitive fighting instincts, still nurtured an urge to return, literally, to nature.

Germany, 1685. The print is a record of an 'enchanted' wolf, which carried off and ate several children. It was finally trapped in a well near Eschenbach on October 9, and killed. An effigy of the wolf, clothed as a man, was hung nearby, clearly establishing its identity as a form of werewolf; a person with the power to assume wolf form at will, or one transformed thus by bewitchment. In most cases the taste for human flesh accompanies the change, and the werewolf hunts by night, devouring human beings. According to European folklore, the werewolf must doff its skin, hide it, and assume human form at daybreak. If he hides it in a cold place, the owner shivers all day; if it is found and destroyed, he dies.

Animals at war

Long ago, deep in prehistory, early man discovered that rocks, spears, bows and arrows were just as handy for eliminating rivals and inconvenient neighbours as for bringing in the next meal. This was the invention of war—a pastime to which man applied himself with a gusto still with us today. And it is intriguing to look back at the varying success and failure with which man has roped in animals to improve his technique in making war.

The horse surely defies all comers as top of the military league. Horse soldiers have a history as old as that of armies in battle, and the type of warhorse has changed with the methods of soldiering on horseback. Originally carrying lightly-armoured swordsmen or lancers, successive generations of warhorses had to carry increasingly heavily-armoured knights, finally having to endure armour themselves as well as the weight of the plate-armoured juggernaut knights of the 14th and 15th centuries.

as well as submachine-guns. Renegade Cossack horsemen served with the German army; and as in 1918 one of the last actions of the Second World War was a cavalry charge.

But horses have also served for many centuries in a less glamorous role, as beasts of burden—dragging guns, and wagons for ammunition, stores and wounded. As readers of Kipling's tale *Her Majesty's Servants* will recall, horses have been joined in this task by draught oxen, mules and camels.

Camels, of course, have always been associated with war in the desert. To the Bedouin Arab the welfare of his camel was as important as the mounts of any regular cavalry regiment. Arab irregulars under Lawrence depended on camel-power for their incredible desert marches against the Turks in the First World War. Regular camel corps were a feature of the Imperial British Army—and even the Red Army of Trotsky and Stalin retained its Turkoman camel corps.

Elephants, too, have long been found both

Verdun in 1916 was awarded the *Légion d'Honneur*! Stuffed with full military honours, it was then solemnly exhibited in a Paris museum for the inspiration of later generations of Frenchmen. And in November 1941 a South African tank commander in the 8th Army had a messenger pigeon alight on his shoulder on the eve of a battle with Rommel's Afrika Korps. Wondering if the bird was carrying the fate of the desert war on its leg, the commander unfolded the message with bated breath—only to read an extremely rude version (in English) of 'Damn you, leave me alone'.

The suicide dogs

Even the dog has played its part on the battlefield. Before achieving immortality in Italy's fight for freedom, Garibaldi had already won a reputation as a sort of 19th-century Fidel Castro, fighting with South American revolutionaries. One of his comrades in this period was a splendid military freelancer who went into battle with a disciplined but formidable pack of large New-

△ *The imprint of modern war: gas-masks for horse and man on the First World War's Western Front. Cavalry troopers were drilled to understand that their mounts were far more important than they were.*

Imperial War Museum

△ *1943: Russian cavalry head into the charge—backed up by tanks and air cover. Horsed cavalry was still very much in use at this time, even though the armies were equipped with tanks, machine-guns and aeroplanes.*

Then the musket and the cannon numbered the days of useful body armour. Faster, less heavily-built horses were needed to keep up with the battlefield fad glamorised as 'charging home with the steel' at full gallop. Armies became professional state institutions instead of freelance levies raised in emergencies. By the 19th and early 20th centuries, cavalry chargers were valuable investments with every army. Cavalry troopers were drilled to understand that their mounts were far more important than themselves; the trooper's duty was to put the health and comfort of his mount on a par with his own—above it if necessary.

Modern uses

Horsed cavalry was still very much in use in the Second World War. In the age of the machine-gun, the dive-bomber, and the tank, the German army included a full cavalry division when it invaded Russia in 1941; the Russians themselves used mass Cossack cavalry forces, armed with sabres

on the battlefield and in the baggage-train. In 218 BC Hannibal included 37 elephants in the hotch-potch confederate Carthaginian army which he led against Rome; but only one—which he was supposed to have used as his personal transport—survived the arduous crossing of the Alps. And the Waterloo of the Rome/Carthage struggle—the Battle of Zama in 202 BC—opened with a mass Carthaginian 'tank attack' by 80 war elephants. In a battle decided by the cavalry of the Romans and their Tunisian allies, the elephants' only success was in roughing-up the lightly-armed skirmishers screening the Roman line. At the other end of the time scale we find elephants at war in the vicious Burma jungle campaigns of 1942-45, used as bulldozers and heavy-duty transports by British and Japanese alike.

Among the animal lightweights, pride of place is held by the carrier pigeon, long used as a swift and unobtrusive battlefield messenger. One pigeon which fell dead after carrying a vital message through the hell of

foundland dogs, trained to savage dismounted enemy horsemen! Dogs were used to lay cable in 1914-18 trench warfare, carrying miniature reels on their backs. And in the Second World War German tank crews were astonished to encounter Russian 'mine dogs'. These canine Kamikazes had been trained to eat only under a tank with its engine running. Taken into the front line (the hungrier the better) with explosives strapped to its back, the mine dog was released toward the German lines, immolating itself under a German tank and—the Russians hoped—taking the tank with it.

For all animals life is a battle—and man is no exception. His earliest combat briefing can be found in Genesis: 'Replenish the earth, and subdue it; and have dominion over the fish of the sea, and over the fowl of the air, and over every living thing that moveth upon the earth.' Well, man has done his best to obey to the letter when it comes to making war—but it would be interesting to have the animals' viewpoint. . . .

'Let slip the dogs of war (and anything else we can use) . . .'

Dogs as beasts of burden, dragging machine-guns for the quaintly-uniformed Belgian infantry in the opening months of the First World War.

Out in No-man's-land, a dog performs the vital job of laying field-telephone cable in the First World War. A dog presents a less obvious target than a man—and is more dispensable . . .

Pachyderm bulldozers. Elephants lay down the foundation logs of the first elephant-built bridge for Slim's 14th Army in Burma.

Underwater photography

Scientists assure us that we need to be cautious in attributing human feelings and behaviour patterns to the wildlife kingdom – yet many times in the course of underwater photography, both in British waters and abroad, I have found that emotions like ours seem to be the only explanation for the behaviour of marine life.

It was the sight of a large fish impaled on my spear during my days as a spear-fisherman that turned me from spear to camera. That fish turned its head round to me and the piteous look in its eyes, more than the glowing gobbets of red blood floating in the water nearby, sickened me of the hunt.

Many of today's underwater photographers have – like many land hunters – turned their age-old hunting instinct to the idea of capturing such creatures permanently on film. From their earlier spearfishing they have brought to underwater photography the knowledge that snapshooting is often the only answer in a medium where the slowest fish can easily outswim the diver photographer.

Yet even this knowledge can be forgotten in the excitement of the moment.

The best picture I didn't take came as I was snorkelling (mask, breathing tube and fins only) slowly along in 10 ft of water just off the English south coast. Visibility was good enough to see the bottom from the surface by inches. Then he retreated – fortunately – into some nearby weed and buried his great body in it. All that I could see of him on my next dive was two huge claws sticking straight up at me, their white undersides making the sight even more off-putting.

It was the picture of a lifetime and with a caption 'Wanna fight?' would surely have won a gold medal. But I didn't take it and continued trying to get him into the boat with supper in mind. I know they say it's wrong to attribute human feelings to such a creature, but the whole attitude of that lobster – even to the moment when he decided to retreat backwards so fast that I lost him – was one of pure irritation that anything should have had the damned cheek to attack him.

Human characteristics

Other lobsters display other human characteristics. They always respond to the underwater photographer's trick of tapping the rock outside their holes – by coming out to look. What can that be but curiosity? One which lives in a sunken Mulberry unit that never reached the Arromanches beach of D-Day in June 1944 is so consumed with this human failing of curiosity that he always walks right up to the head of the flash unit as I thread it among the twisted girders that guard his home 40 ft deep, 2 miles off the Sussex coast.

Fish, too, I'm sure, are prone to show this selves to be touched. But once again, they can be handled if so harassed that they actually surrender. I had this happen while diving in Cornwall on the Manacle Rocks. My wife was first to spot the beautifully marked John Dory which hovered above the tangle of green and brown kelp like a helicopter with desert-warfare markings. It would be impossible to mistake the John Dory for anything else. Apart from the great black 'thumb-mark' on his sides (where St Peter is meant to have handled him when extracting the tribute-money from his mouth) his brilliant blue eyes give him away at once.

I had been trying to get photographs of this beautiful fish for some time and now here was one right before me. My wife acted as a sort of underwater sheep-dog, driving the hovering fish nearer and nearer to the closeup lens of my camera.

For a long time he resisted this shepherding back and forward until suddenly it seemed he was tired of his darting attempts to escape and, like an exhausted human being, surrendered – having his picture taken from whichever angle I wanted. He hung there so still that I reached out a finger and stroked him down the underside of his 'chin' (it is this 'chin' which extends into a telescopic mouth as many a small fish has realised too late). Then he made one more dash for freedom and we didn't try to stop him.

And what a fellow for human feelings is

Closeup of Mediterranean bream: this school of curious fish was attracted by the expired air bubbles from the photographer's aqualung.

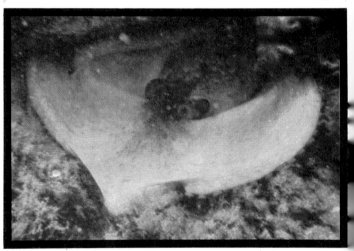

Pale with fear? If disturbed, octopuses go white or flush red, then they grip the rock with rear tentacles, leaving the others free for defence.

face, if a trifle mistily. Suddenly beneath me I saw the great black shape of a lobster – and his size made me gasp. He looked nearly 3 ft long as he moved down a gully in between the hard clay banks that were the bottom in this area. Forgetting all about the camera which was slung round my neck I determined to try and pin him down to the bottom with a metal rod I carried and then grab him from the back where his claws couldn't get at me.

I slid down gently from the surface – and he still hadn't seen me. His great claws – both looked bigger than my hands – were folded neatly in a triangle, point-to-point in front of him. When I was on his level I moved the rod forward to pin him to the seabed – and he attacked me! With a swishing right hook and a left cross that would have done credit to Cassius Clay, he missed emotion. On that same sunken Mulberry unit, their dark brown bodies startlingly banded with silvery-white hues, pouting wheel around you in such numbers that on occasions you actually have to push them out of the way with your hands to get enough clear water to take photographs. Yet these are obviously the youngsters of the fish world. The older pouting, who have lost their banding and are coppery-brown all over, treat masked visitors from above with much more caution.

They lurk in the dark passageways that tangle through the ruined Mulberry and seldom venture far from such safety. To get pictures of these you have to go in after them with flash. They are cautious, wise old things – but there I go again, giving fish human attributes!

Fish, it is true, do not usually allow them-the octopus. In the Mediterranean at the determined approach of the cameraman he will often go white (with fear?) or flush red (with anger?).

Some fish, in Spain for example, wheel about above the seabed in big shoals, but rarely let the underwater photographer get close enough to get a really effective shot. I'm afraid that the spear-fishermen of these clear waters have a lot to answer for. But I found that you could lure big shoals of saupe (a Mediterranean bream) close enough for effective pictures if you sat quite still on the bottom looking down at the seabed. When you sensed the fish were close, you whipped the camera up and fired at the same instant right into the heart of the shoal. And what human activity were those fish indulging in? Why, hide-and-seek, of course!

Peter Hill

△ *Setting the scene. Black and white damselfishes, with butterfly fishes above, swim over living, wavy brown pavana coral, a favourite habitat. Although they were photographed in an aquarium this is the kind of delightful setting the underwater photographer hopes to encounter.*
▽ *Sitting down on the job: these pouting off the English Sussex coast have no fear of man and obligingly circle round the photographer.*

Kendall McDonald

Authors

Alfred Saunders

Terms of reference
The scientific classification of animals — Dr Maurice Burton
Brand names in animal life — Dr Maurice Burton
The division between the plant and
  animal kingdoms — TBB Paddock
Ultrastructure of animal cells — Geoffrey Rowden
Cell division: mitosis and meiosis — T White

Evolution
Darwin — Cathy Jarman
Evolution of man — Dr Colin Groves
Dinosaurs — Carolyn Barber
Evolution in action — Dr HBD Kettlewell
Bird speciation — Dr David Snow
Genetics of the black panther — Ray Robinson
Albinism — Carolyn Barber

Adaptation and longevity
Protective coloration — Cathy Jarman
Colours of animals — Gwynne Vevers
Poisonous butterflies and moths — Miriam Rothschild
Flight in animals — Cathy Jarman
Life-span of animals — David Le Roi
Insect life histories — Michael Tweedie
The metamorphosis of insects — Sir Vincent Wigglesworth

Organs of special sense
Animal eyes and their ways of life — Constance P Warner
Eyes of insects — Anthony Bannister

Electric organs in fishes — Dr KE Banister
Butterfly courtship — L Hugh Newman

The geography of animals
South American animals — Dr Barbara Weir
The fauna of New Zealand — Dr MF Soper
The Galapagos — Caroline Weaver

Ecology
Polar environments and life — Ronald I Lewis Smith
Life in the deeps — Dr NB Marshall
Plankton — Peter D Parks
Pond life — John Clegg

Conservation
Man in animal life — Peter Scott
Pollution and animal life — Stanley Cramp
Conservation and breeding of rare
  pheasants — Fred Johnson
Sea turtle conservation — Dr H Robert Bustard
Serengeti today — David Houston

Man and animals
Animals in magic — Malcom Saunders
Lycanthropy — Frank Smythe
Animals at war — Richard Humble
Underwater photography — Kendall McDonald

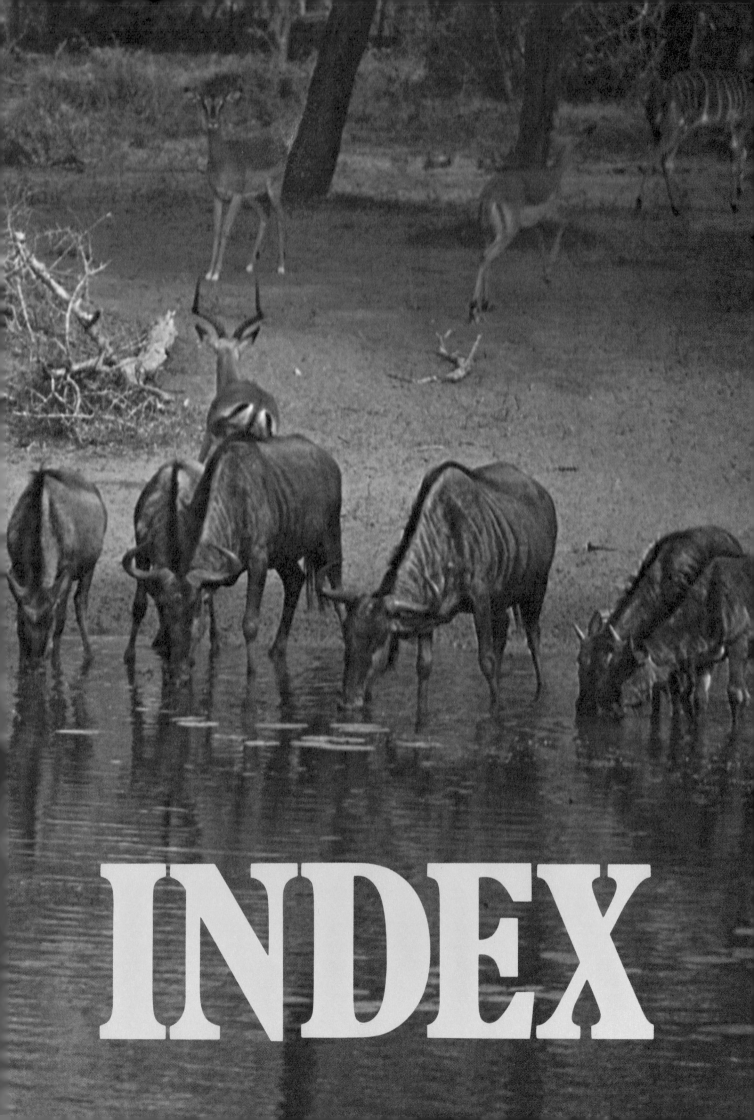

INDEX

Contents and key: This index is arranged in three sections; an **Animal Index,** an alphabetical list of common and Latin animal names, a **Subject Index** and an animal classification, the **Systematic Index.** Common names and numbers in bold type indicate that there is a complete article on that animal. Numbers in italic type indicate an illustration. Numbers in bold italic type indicate a complete, illustrated article, * indicates a distribution map, † indicates a cross reference. The systematic index reads horizontally from phylum to family. Names in italic type indicate a subdivision.

Vol 1 1 – 140   Vol 2 141 – 280   Vol 3 281 – 420   Vol 4 421 – 560   Vol 5 561 – 700   Vol 6 701 – 840   Vol 7 841 – 980   Vol 8 981 – 1120   Vol 9 1121 – 1260   Vol 10 1261 – 1400

Vol 11 1401 – 1540   Vol 12 1541 – 1680   Vol 13 1681 – 1820   Vol 14 1821 – 1960   Vol 15 1961 – 2100   Vol 16 2101 – 2240   Vol 17 2241 – 2380   Vol 18 2381 – 2520   Vol 19 2521 – 2660   Vol 20 2661 – 2800

2771

Vol 1 1—140   Vol 2 141—280   Vol 3 281—420   Vol 4 421—560   Vol 5 561—700   Vol 6 701—840   Vol 7 841—980   Vol 8 981—1120   Vol 9 1121—1260   Vol 10 1261—1400
Vol 11 1401—1540   Vol 12 1541—1680   Vol 13 1681—1820   Vol 14 1821—1960   Vol 15 1961—2100   Vol 16 2101—2240   Vol 17 2241—2380   Vol 18 2381—2520   Vol 19 2521—2660   Vol 20 2661—2800

2772

Vol 1 1—140   Vol 2 141—280   Vol 3 281—420   Vol 4 421—560   Vol 5 561—700   Vol 6 701—840   Vol 7 841—980   Vol 8 981—1120   Vol 9 1121—1260   Vol 10 1261—1400

Vol 11 1401—1540   Vol 12 1541—1680   Vol 13 1681—1820   Vol 14 1821—1960   Vol 15 1961—2100   Vol 16 2101—2240   Vol 17 2241—2380   Vol 18 2381—2520   Vol 19 2521—2660   Vol 20 2661—2800

2773

| Vol 1 1–140 | Vol 2 141–280 | Vol 3 281–420 | Vol 4 421–560 | Vol 5 561–700 | Vol 6 701–840 | Vol 7 841–980 | Vol 8 981–1120 | Vol 9 1121–1260 | Vol 10 1261–1400 |

| Vol 11 1401–1540 | Vol 12 1541–1680 | Vol 13 1681–1820 | Vol 14 1821–1960 | Vol 15 1961–2100 | Vol 16 2101–2240 | Vol 17 2241–2380 | Vol 18 2381–2520 | Vol 19 2521–2660 | Vol 20 2661–2800 |

2774

Vol 1 1−140   Vol 2 141−280   Vol 3 281−420   Vol 4 421−560   Vol 5 561−700   Vol 6 701−840   Vol 7 841−980   Vol 8 981−1120   Vol 9 1121−1260   Vol 10 1261−1400
Vol 11 1401−1540   Vol 12 1541−1680   Vol 13 1681−1820   Vol 14 1821−1960   Vol 15 1961−2100   Vol 16 2101−2240   Vol 17 2241−2380   Vol 18 2381−2520   Vol 19 2521−2660   Vol 20 2661−2800

2775

Vol 1 1–140   Vol 2 141–280   Vol 3 281–420   Vol 4 421–560   Vol 5 561–700   Vol 6 701–840   Vol 7 841–980   Vol 8 981–1120   Vol 9 1121–1260   Vol 10 1261–1400
Vol 11 1401–1540   Vol 12 1541–1680   Vol 13 1681–1820   Vol 14 1821–1960   Vol 15 1961–2100   Vol 16 2101–2240   Vol 17 2241–2380   Vol 18 2381–2520   Vol 19 2521–2660   Vol 20 2661–2800

2776

Vol 1 1—140 Vol 2 141—280 Vol 3 281—420 Vol 4 421—560 Vol 5 561—700 Vol 6 701—840 Vol 7 841—980 Vol 8 981—1120 Vol 9 1121—1260 Vol 10 1261—1400
Vol 11 1401—1540 Vol 12 1541—1680 Vol 13 1681—1820 Vol 14 1821—1960 Vol 15 1961—2100 Vol 16 2101—2240 Vol 17 2241—2380 Vol 18 2381—2520 Vol 19 2521—2660 Vol 20 2661—2800

2777

Vol 1 1 – 140   **Vol 2** 141 – 280   **Vol 3** 281 – 420   **Vol 4** 421 – 560   **Vol 5** 561 – 700   **Vol 6** 701 – 840   **Vol 7** 841 – 980   **Vol 8** 981 – 1120   **Vol 9** 1121 – 1260   **Vol 10** 1261 – 1400

Vol 11 1401 – 1540   **Vol 12** 1541 – 1680   **Vol 13** 1681 – 1820   **Vol 14** 1821 – 1960   **Vol 15** 1961 – 2100   **Vol 16** 2101 – 2240   **Vol 17** 2241 – 2380   **Vol 18** 2381 – 2520   **Vol 19** 2521 – 2660   **Vol 20** 2661 – 2800

2778

Vol 1 1 – 140   Vol 2 141 – 280   Vol 3 281 – 420   Vol 4 421 – 560   Vol 5 561 – 700   Vol 6 701 – 840   Vol 7 841 – 980   Vol 8 981 – 1120   Vol 9 1121 – 1260   Vol 10 1261 – 1400
Vol 11 1401 – 1540   Vol 12 1541 – 1680   Vol 13 1681 – 1820   Vol 14 1821 – 1960   Vol 15 1961 – 2100   Vol 16 2101 – 2240   Vol 17 2241 – 2380   Vol 18 2381 – 2520   Vol 19 2521 – 2660   Vol 20 2661 – 2800

2779

Vol 1 1 – 140   Vol 2 141 – 280   Vol 3 281 – 420   Vol 4 421 – 560   Vol 5 561 – 700   Vol 6 701 – 840   Vol 7 841 – 980   Vol 8 981 – 1120   Vol 9 1121 – 1260   Vol 10 1261 – 1400

Vol 11 1401 – 1540   Vol 12 1541 – 1680   Vol 13 1681 – 1820   Vol 14 1821 – 1960   Vol 15 1961 – 2100   Vol 16 2101 – 2240   Vol 17 2241 – 2380   Vol 18 2381 – 2520   Vol 19 2521 – 2660   Vol 20 2661 – 2800

2780

1–140   Vol 2 141–280   Vol 3 281–420   Vol 4 421–560   Vol 5 561–700   Vol 6 701–840   Vol 7 841–980   Vol 8 981–1120   Vol 9 1121–1260   Vol 10 1261–1400
11 1401–1540   Vol 12 1541–1680   Vol 13 1681–1820   Vol 14 1821–1960   Vol 15 1961–2100   Vol 16 2101–2240   Vol 17 2241–2380   Vol 18 2381–2520   Vol 19 2521–2660   Vol 20 2661–2800

2781

Vol 1 1—140   Vol 2 141—280   Vol 3 281—420   Vol 4 421—560   Vol 5 561—700   Vol 6 701—840   Vol 7 841—980   Vol 8 981—1120   Vol 9 1121—1260   Vol 10 1261—1400

Vol 11 1401—1540   Vol 12 1541—1680   Vol 13 1681—1820   Vol 14 1821—1960   Vol 15 1961—2100   Vol 16 2101—2240   Vol 17 2241—2380   Vol 18 2381—2520   Vol 19 2521—2660   Vol 20 2661—2800

2782

Vol 1 1−140   Vol 2 141−280   Vol 3 281−420   Vol 4 421−560   Vol 5 561−700   Vol 6 701−840   Vol 7 841−980   Vol 8 981−1120   Vol 9 1121−1260   Vol 10 1261−1400
Vol 11 1401−1540   Vol 12 1541−1680   Vol 13 1681−1820   Vol 14 1821−1960   Vol 15 1961−2100   Vol 16 2101−2240   Vol 17 2241−2380   Vol 18 2381−2520   Vol 19 2521−2660   Vol 20 2661−2800

2783

Vol 1 1 — 140   Vol 2 141 — 280   Vol 3 281 — 420   Vol 4 421 — 560   Vol 5 561 — 700   Vol 6 701 — 840   Vol 7 841 — 980   Vol 8 981 — 1120   Vol 9 1121 — 1260   Vol 10 1261 — 1400

Vol 11 1401 — 1540   Vol 12 1541 — 1680   Vol 13 1681 — 1820   Vol 14 1821 — 1960   Vol 15 1961 — 2100   Vol 16 2101 — 2240   Vol 17 2241 — 2380   Vol 18 2381 — 2520   Vol 19 2521 — 2660   Vol 20 2661 — 2800

2784

Vol 1 1—140   Vol 2 141—280   Vol 3 281—420   Vol 4 421—560   Vol 5 561—700   Vol 6 701—840   Vol 7 841—980   Vol 8 981—1120   Vol 9 1121—1260   Vol 10 1261—1400
Vol 11 1401—1540   Vol 12 1541—1680   Vol 13 1681—1820   Vol 14 1821—1960   Vol 15 1961—2100   Vol 16 2101—2240   Vol 17 2241—2380   Vol 18 2381—2520   Vol 19 2521—2660   Vol 20 2661—2800

2785

Vol 1 1—140   Vol 2 141—280   Vol 3 281—420   Vol 4 421—560   Vol 5 561—700   Vol 6 701—840   Vol 7 841—980   Vol 8 981—1120   Vol 9 1121—1260   Vol 10 1261—1400

Vol 11 1401—1540   Vol 12 1541—1680   Vol 13 1681—1820   Vol 14 1821—1960   Vol 15 1961—2100   Vol 16 2101—2240   Vol 17 2241—2380   Vol 18 2381—2520   Vol 19 2521—2660   Vol 20 2661—2800

2786

Vol 1 1 – 140   Vol 2 141 – 280   Vol 3 281 – 420   Vol 4 421 – 560   Vol 5 561 – 700   Vol 6 701 – 840   Vol 7 841 – 980   Vol 8 981 – 1120   Vol 9 1121 – 1260   Vol 10 1261 – 1400

Vol 11 1401 – 1540   Vol 12 1541 – 1680   Vol 13 1681 – 1820   Vol 14 1821 – 1960   Vol 15 1961 – 2100   Vol 16 2101 – 2240   Vol 17 2241 – 2380   Vol 18 2381 – 2520   Vol 19 2521 – 2660   Vol 20 2661 – 2800

2787

Vol 1 1 – 140   Vol 2 141 – 280   Vol 3 281 – 420   Vol 4 421 – 560   Vol 5 561 – 700   Vol 6 701 – 840   Vol 7 841 – 980   Vol 8 981 – 1120   Vol 9 1121 – 1260   Vol 10 1261 – 1400
Vol 11 1401 – 1540   Vol 12 1541 – 1680   Vol 13 1681 – 1820   Vol 14 1821 – 1960   Vol 15 1961 – 2100   Vol 16 2101 – 2240   Vol 17 2241 – 2380   Vol 18 2381 – 2520   Vol 19 2521 – 2660   Vol 20 2661 – 2800

2788

Vol 1 1—140   Vol 2 141—280   Vol 3 281—420   Vol 4 421—560   Vol 5 561—700   Vol 6 701—840   Vol 7 841—980   Vol 8 981—1120   Vol 9 1121—1260   Vol 10 1261—1400
Vol 11 1401—1540   Vol 12 1541—1680   Vol 13 1681—1820   Vol 14 1821—1960   Vol 15 1961—2100   Vol 16 2101—2240   Vol 17 2241—2380   Vol 18 2381—2520   Vol 19 2521—2660   Vol 20 2661—2800

2789

Vol 1 1–140   Vol 2 141–280   Vol 3 281–420   Vol 4 421–560   Vol 5 561–700   Vol 6 701–840   Vol 7 841–980   Vol 8 981–1120   Vol 9 1121–1260   Vol 10 1261–1400

Vol 11 1401–1540   Vol 12 1541–1680   Vol 13 1681–1820   Vol 14 1821–1960   Vol 15 1961–2100   Vol 16 2101–2240   Vol 17 2241–2380   Vol 18 2381–2520   Vol 19 2521–2660   Vol 20 2661–2800

2790

Vol 1 1–140   Vol 2 141–280   Vol 3 281–420   Vol 4 421–560   Vol 5 561–700   Vol 6 701–840   Vol 7 841–980   Vol 8 981–1120   Vol 9 1121–1260   Vol 10 1261–1400

Vol 11 1401–1540   Vol 12 1541–1680   Vol 13 1681–1820   Vol 14 1821–1960   Vol 15 1961–2100   Vol 16 2101–2240   Vol 17 2241–2380   Vol 18 2381–2520   Vol 19 2521–2660   Vol 20 2661–2800

2792

Vol 1 1—140   Vol 2 141—280   Vol 3 281—420   Vol 4 421—560   Vol 5 561—700   Vol 6 701—840   Vol 7 841—980   Vol 8 981—1120   Vol 9 1121—1260   Vol 10 1261—1400

Vol 11 1401—1540   Vol 12 1541—1680   Vol 13 1681—1820   Vol 14 1821—1960   Vol 15 1961—2100   Vol 16 2101—2240   Vol 17 2241—2380   Vol 18 2381—2520   Vol 19 2521—2660   Vol 20 2661—2800

2793

Vol 1 1—140   **Vol 2** 141—280   **Vol 3** 281—420   **Vol 4** 421—560   **Vol 5** 561—700   **Vol 6** 701—840   **Vol 7** 841—980   **Vol 8** 981—1120   **Vol 9** 1121—1260   **Vol 10** 1261—1400

Vol 11 1401—1540   **Vol 12** 1541—1680   **Vol 13** 1681—1820   **Vol 14** 1821—1960   **Vol 15** 1961—2100   **Vol 16** 2101—2240   **Vol 17** 2241—2380   **Vol 18** 2381—2520   **Vol 19** 2521—2660   **Vol 20** 2661—2800

2794

Vol 1 1–140   Vol 2 141–280   Vol 3 281–420   Vol 4 421–560   Vol 5 561–700   Vol 6 701–840   Vol 7 841–980   Vol 8 981–1120   Vol 9 1121–1260   Vol 10 1261–1400
Vol 11 1401–1540   Vol 12 1541–1680   Vol 13 1681–1820   Vol 14 1821–1960   Vol 15 1961–2100   Vol 16 2101–2240   Vol 17 2241–2380   Vol 18 2381–2520   Vol 19 2521–2660   Vol 20 2661–2800

2795

Systematic Index

Vol 1 1–140   Vol 2 141–280   Vol 3 281–420   Vol 4 421–560   Vol 5 561–700   Vol 6 701–840   Vol 7 841–980   Vol 8 981–1120   Vol 9 1121–1260   Vol 10 1261–1400

Vol 11 1401–1540   Vol 12 1541–1680   Vol 13 1681–1820   Vol 14 1821–1960   Vol 15 1961–2100   Vol 16 2101–2240   Vol 17 2241–2380   Vol 18 2381–2520   Vol 19 2521–2660   Vol 20 2661–2800

2796

Systematic Index

Phylum	Class	Order	Family
			Noctuidae 257 1651
			Notodontidae 1850 1872
			Nymphalidae 823 1207 1869 2519
			Olethreutidae 480
			Papilionidae 73 206 2323
			Pieridae 2608
			Prodoxidae 2670
			Psychidae 125
			Pterophoridae 1797
			Pyralididae 1379
			Saturniidae 103
			Satyridae 1446
			Sphingidae 1047
			Tinaeidae 456
			Uraniidae 2514
			Zygaenidae 317
		Diptera	Asilidae 1967
			Calliphoridae 242
			Cecidomyidae 1458
			Chironomidae 1458
			Culicidae 1512
			Drosophilidae 830
			Muscidae 1126 2483
			Phoridae 484
			Syrphidae 1133
			Tabanidae 1120
			Tachinidae 2346
			Tipulidae 603
		Siphonaptera 782	
		Hymenoptera 1711	Apidae 1090
			Bombidae 311
			Braconidae 1161
			Chalcidae 408
			Cimbicidae 2027
			Cynipoidea 842
			Dorylinae 88
			Formicidae 2632
			Camponotinae 1085
			Dolichoderinae 1085
			Myrmicinae 1036 1288
			Ichneumonidae 1161
			Megachilidae 1290
			Mutillidae 2524
			Pompilidae 1144
			Sphecidae 1144
			Vespidae 1112 1144 1694 2564
	Crustacea		
	Branchiopoda	Anostraca	Chirocephalidae 729
		Cladocerca	Daphniidae 612
	Copepoda 519	Branchiura	Argulidae 771
	Cirripedia	Rhizocephala 2005	
		Thoracica 145	
	Malacostraca	Mysidacea	Mysidae 1619
		Isopoda 2168 2644	
		Amphipoda 36	
		Stomatopoda 1409	
		Euphausiacea 1261	
		Decapoda 1334 1965 2225 2249	Cancridae 685
			Coenobitidae 1057
			Paguridae 1057
			Palaemonidae 1845
			Parastacidae 564
			Potamobiidae 564
			Portunidae 2128
		Brachyura 1477	
		Natantia 2134	
		Reptantia 754	
	Merostoma	Xiphosura 1228	
	Arachnida 1723	Scorpiones 2047	
		Pseudoscorpiones 736	
		Solifugae 2207	
		Opiliones	Phalangidae 1034
		Araneae 1628	Agelenidae 2116 2574
			Aviculariidae 199
			Barychelidae 2446
			Ctenizidae 2446
			Lycosidae 2366 2624
			Pisauridae 2624
			Sparassidae 559
			Theridiidae 232
			Thomisidae 559
		Acarina 1473 2412	
	Pycnogonida 2085		
	Tardigrada 2368		
Chaetognatha 92			
Pogonophora		Athecanephria 1804	
		Thecanephria 1804	

Phylum	Class	Order	Family
Echinodermata	Crinoidea	Articulata 2069	Ammodytidae 2016
			Antedonidae 2069
	Holothuroidea 2060		
	Echinoidea 2094	Clypeasteroida 2015	
	Asteroidea	Phanerozonia 2261	
	Ophiuroidea	Euryalae	Euryalidae 157
		Ophiurae 288	
Chordata			
Hemichordata 10			
Urochordata		Ascidacea 2090	
		Thaliacea 1876 2014	
		Larvacea 2090	
Cephalochordata			Branchiostomidae 1278
Vertebrata	Marsipobranchii	Hyperoartii	Petromyzontidae 1276
		Hyperotreta	Myxinidae 1003
	Selachii	Hypotremata	Dasyatidae 2279
			Myliobatidae 676
			Pristidae 2025
			Rajidae 2150
			Rhjnobatidae 987
		Heterodontiformes	Heterodontidae 1827
		Pleurotremata	Alopiidae 2404
			Cacharhinidae 2671
			Cetorhinidae 159
			Chlamydoselachidae 820
			Isuridae 1395 1822
			Orectolobidae 2618
			Rhincodontidae 2599
			Scyliorhinidae 397 651
			Sphyrnidae 1015
			Squalidae 651
			Squatinidae 1496
		Batoidei	Mobulidae 629
			Torpedinidae 707
	Bradyodonti		
	Holocephali	Chimaerae 427	
	Pisces	Acipenseriformes (Chondrostei)	Acipensidae 2296
			Polyodontidae 1670
		Cladistia	Polypteridae 192
		Protospondyli	Amiidae 279
		Ginglymodi	Lepisosteidae 846
		Clupeiformes	Clupeidae 1064 1451 1762 2105
			Engraulidae 43
		Elopiformes	Megalopidae 2369
		Salmoniformes	Alepisauridae 1279
			Chauliodontidae 2531
			Esocidae 1761
			Gonostomatidae 283
			Harpodontidae 258
			Myctophidae 1284
			Osmeridae 2180
			Paralepididae 155
			Plecoglossidae 2335
			Salmonidae 101 937 1667 2472
			Sternoptychidae 1041
			Umbridae 1524
		Gonorynchidae	Chanidae 1460
		Osteoglossiformes	Notopteridae 741 1250
			Osteoglossidae 77
			Pantodontidae 339
		Mormyriformes	Gymnarchidae 1578
			Mormyridae 1578
		Haplomi	Dallidae 23
		Cetomimiformes	Cetomimidae 2597
			Giganturidae 881
		Siluriformes	Callichthyidae 86
			Doradidae 86
			Loricariidae 86 1071
			Malapteruridae 704
			Siluridae 395
		Anguilliformes	Anguillidae 689
			Congridae 515
			Eurypharyngidae 988
			Monognathidae 988
			Muraenidae 1507
			Saccopharyngidae 988
		Percopsiformes	Percopsidae 2473
		Gasterosteiformes	Aulorhynchidae 2488
			Centriscidae 2135
			Gasterosteidae 2273
			Syngnathidae 1772 2066
		Cypriniformes	Apteronotidae 1250

Vol 1 1—140 Vol 2 141—280 Vol 3 281—420 Vol 4 421—560 Vol 5 561—700 Vol 6 701—840 Vol 7 841—980 Vol 8 981—1120 Vol 9 1121—1260 Vol 10 1261—1400
Vol 11 1401—1540 Vol 12 1541—1680 Vol 13 1681—1820 Vol 14 1821—1960 Vol 15 1961—2100 Vol 16 2101—2240 Vol 17 2241—2380 Vol 18 2381—2520 Vol 19 2521—2660 Vol 20 2661—2800

2797

Systematic Index

Vol 1 1– 140   Vol 2 141– 280   Vol 3 281– 420   Vol 4 421– 560   Vol 5 561– 700   Vol 6 701– 840   Vol 7 841– 980   Vol 8 981– 1120   Vol 9 1121– 1260   Vol 10 1261– 1400

Vol 11 1401– 1540   Vol 12 1541– 1680   Vol 13 1681– 1820   Vol 14 1821– 1960   Vol 15 1961– 2100   Vol 16 2101– 2240   Vol 17 2241– 2380   Vol 18 2381– 2520   Vol 19 2521– 2660   Vol 20 2661– 2800

2798

Systematic Index

1 1–140   Vol 2 141–280   Vol 3 281–420   Vol 4 421–560   Vol 5 561–700   Vol 6 701–840   Vol 7 841–980   Vol 8 981–1120   Vol 9 1121–1260   Vol 10 1261–1400

11 1401–1540   Vol 12 1541–1680   Vol 13 1681–1820   Vol 14 1821–1960   Vol 15 1961–2100   Vol 16 2101–2240   Vol 17 2241–2380   Vol 18 2381–2520   Vol 19 2521–2660   Vol 20 2661–2800

2799

Systematic Index

Vol 1 1–140   Vol 2 141–280   Vol 3 281–420   Vol 4 421–560   Vol 5 561–700   Vol 6 701–840   Vol 7 841–980   Vol 8 981–1120   Vol 9 1121–1260   Vol 10 1261–1400

Vol 11 1401–1540   Vol 12 1541–1680   Vol 13 1681–1820   Vol 14 1821–1960   Vol 15 1961–2100   Vol 16 2101–2240   Vol 17 2241–2380   Vol 18 2381–2520   Vol 19 2521–2660   Vol 20 2661–2800

2800